WE KEEP A PUB

*

Tom Berkley

We Keep a Pub

With illustrations by
STARKE

ARROW BOOKS

ARROW BOOKS LTD
178–202 Great Portland Street, London W1

AN IMPRINT OF THE HUTCHINSON GROUP

London Melbourne Sydney
Auckland Bombay Toronto
Johannesburg New York

✳

First published by
Hutchinson & Co. (*Publishers*) Ltd. 1955
First Arrow edition 1957
Reprinted 1958
Reprinted 1959
Reprinted 1961
Reprinted November 1967

*Made and printed in Great Britain
by The Anchor Press, Ltd.,
Tiptree, Essex*

I

WE were sitting side by side in a small waiting-room, and feeling somewhat nervous.

'Bill,' whispered Irene.

'Yes?'

'Don't forget to call them "sir".'

'No fear!'

'Be careful, won't you? Because you're not used to calling people "sir". You were a bit off-hand with the last lot.'

'Was I?'

'I thought so. Pretend you're back in the Army.'

'That's an idea.'

'What about me? Ought I to call them "sir"?'

'Oh crikey!' I giggled. 'I never thought of that. What did you do with the others?'

'I didn't,' chuckled Irene. 'I didn't like to.'

'Well, don't with these,' I grinned. 'For heaven's sake don't do anything unnatural, or we'll feel like a couple o' goofs.'

'Righto; I'll let you do it all. What are you staring at?'

I nodded towards a doorway on our right, through which a pair of shapely legs could be seen disappearing up some stairs.

'They've some pretty snappy typists here,' I grinned.

'Yes,' whispered Irene. 'Quite a beauty chorus.'

'Wonder who picks 'em.'

'Perhaps we'll be able to guess at the interview,' smiled Irene.

We both chuckled; and the door on our left opened.

'Will you come in?' said a voice.

Looking round, we saw a pallid thin-lipped man dressed rather like an undertaker, who ushered us into the next room.

Our entrance could not have been stage-managed better. We entered still smiling at our little joke; and the three directors sitting at the long board-room table reacted spontaneously. They all smiled.

At the far end we saw a spare grey-haired man of about

fifty lounging cross-legged on an upright chair. He had blue eyes and a clipped moustache, and at a guess was almost as tall as I am, but lanky instead of broad. He seemed to like the look of us.

The chairman, a tubby old boy with a bald head, sitting at the middle of the table, eyed us in a fatherly manner over the top of his glasses and smiled us to two chairs, while the youngest of the three, a ginger-haired man of about forty, with a handlebar moustache, sitting on his left, grinned sympathetically at us as if to say : I bet you're hating this.

The three of them were smoking cigarettes, though no one thought of asking Irene and me to join them. There was a short silence while we sat down, then the chairman opened the proceedings.

'So you would like to manage one of our houses?' he remarked, still smiling.

'Yes,' said I. Then remembering Irene's wifely warning, I added nervously: 'Er—yes, sir. Rather! Absolutely!'

That amused the directors. The three of them laughed.

Irene and I felt we had made a good first impression. Even the austere individual who had called us into the room gave us a sort of secretarial smirk of encouragement.

'What about you, Mrs. Day?' the chairman asked.

'We both want to,' said Irene.

He eyed her thoughtfully. Irene is an ultra-dainty type, slender, and a hundred per cent feminine.

'Hm! It's hard work, you know.'

'I don't mind that.'

The old boy seemed unconvinced.

'Have you ever done any hard work?' he smiled. 'Really hard work?'

'I drove an ambulance for five years during the war.'

'You stuck it for five years!'

'Yes.'

That went down well, particularly with the two elder directors, who exchanged glances.

'Did you like it?' inquired the tall one at the far end of the table.

'Not very much,' replied Irene with a grimace.

That caused another general laugh.

'But I enjoyed the companionship, the—er—*camaraderie*, you know. That was fun.'

'Ah!—you're a good mixer,' chuckled the chairman. 'That's a point. You have to be a good mixer in this business.'

Irene made no answer to that; and the chairman exchanged glances again with the tall grey-moustached director. To me it seemed their thoughts were running on the same lines. The woman was game, but too dainty, too refined. Pity—because they liked her. But they thought I was tough enough. Big enough too, judging by their expressions. No need for a chucker-out on Saturday nights. Irene could read their thoughts as well as I could, and felt she was letting the side down. I saw her glance at the junior director, as if wishing he would say something. She is no fool, is my Irene.

'Tell me, Mrs. Day,' continued the chairman before the younger man could leap into the breach, 'have you ever visualized a busy Saturday night, or a bank holiday, say, when your husband is occupied in the cellar, or somewhere out of call?'

'Oh, yes,' smiled Irene. 'We've discussed all that. That won't worry me. Don't forget I've lived some years in Malaya.'

'Er—yes, I see,' said the chairman; but he had obviously missed the point, and didn't see at all. He transferred his attention to me. 'You say in your letter you resigned your appointment in Malaya last June. That's nearly a year ago. Have you done anything since then?'

'No, sir,' I replied. 'I've been on the sick list. That's really why I came home. I was wounded.'

'Wounded . . .? Oh, of course! You mentioned that in your application.' He found my letter and quoted from it. ' "*Plantation buildings destroyed by bandits . . . wife only just*

*saved . . . no longer a country for white women . . . officer
during war . . . aged forty . . .*" Mm—yes, I see your point,
Mrs. Day, about living there. You know, Mr. Day, I don't
blame you for throwing it all up, particularly as you're
married. But what made you come to us? This work's so
different.'

'That's rather a long story, sir.'

The three directors signified that they would like to hear it.

'Well, sir, to start with, rubber planting is the only job I
know, and I had to pick something I thought I could do,
and——'

'And you think anyone can be a publican?'

I couldn't very well tell them that that was exactly what
I did think.

'No,' I lied, 'I don't think anyone can be a publican; at
least, not a good one. But I do think I have some of the—er
—what you might call natural qualifications.'

'Such as . . . ?'

'Well, I'm not bad at handling people, sir. I mean, that's
an asset; and it's what we were paid for in Malaya. There's
a permanent labour shortage there. The coolies are recruited
from India, you know; and a planter who can keep his
labour force happy, and make 'em work at the same time,
gets on. There's not much in planting itself. Planters are
paid for handling people.'

'But rather different kind of people from the ones you'll
find in this business.'

'Yes, sir, but the principle is the same; and one had all
kinds in the Army, of course; and—er—I got my majority
in the Army, sir.'

'Book-keeping?' murmured the grey-moustached
director.

'There again the principle is the same,' I smiled. 'Don't you think so, sir—in any business?'

'More or less, so long as you don't get behind with it.'

'Quite, sir!' I beamed disarmingly; for on the plantation all that sort of thing was done by a *kanakapulle*.

The directors nodded and turned their attention to Irene, who gave me a congratulatory nudge with her foot for crossing that bit of country so cleverly.

'Now, what about cooking?' the chairman asked her. 'Can you cook?'

Irene is not fond of cooking. She has quite a gift for planning meals with a native cook, and can even translate Mother Beeton's recipes into Malay or Tamil and make them understandable; but the cooking itself bores her. In fact, to put it bluntly, she hates it.

'Oh, yes—of course!' she replied, as if rather resenting the chairman's question.

'But can you cook well?' he asked.

She fidgeted with one finger.

'That's for other people to say,' she smiled. 'My husband doesn't grumble.'

I looked hastily down at my lap, because her husband had done most of the cooking since he came home from Malaya.

'Well, what about carving?' asked the chairman. 'Could you carve and serve for, say, sixty people?'

The poor girl rocked on her chair.

'Oh, yes,' she replied quietly.

'Suppose the cook was taken ill or something, and didn't come to work one day, and you had to go into the kitchen and cook, and carve, and serve for sixty people . . .?'

But Irene was incapable of visualizing such an appalling catastrophe. Surely no cook could be so heartless !

'Could you do it ?' the chairman persisted.

'Oh, yes, I could do that,' smiled Irene bravely ; 'and—and my husband is a very good cook. He has a sort of flair for it.'

We were rather banking on my flair for cooking. I had done quite a lot of it in odd out-of-the-way spots in my bachelor days ; but the directors seemed uninterested.

'Oh, really ?' said the chairman casually. 'Then we may take it, Mrs. Day, that you do know something about cooking ?'

'Oh, yes—er—definitely !' said Irene in a tone of voice intended to convey the impression that that was an understatement of her abilities.

'You will find restaurant cooking very different from cooking in your own home,' muttered the grey-moustached director.

Irene entirely agreed with him.

'Yes,' she said, 'I expect that.'

'But it's soon picked up,' smiled the chairman encouragingly. 'Only needs a little practice. It's the custom, you understand, to put new couples through a period of training. The husband learns the cellar and the books ; and both serve behind the bars, of course ; and the wife learns the kitchen and the restaurant, and carves at the hot-plate, and so forth. How d'you think you will like all that ?'

'Very much indeed,' lied Irene enthusiastically.

'And you, Mr. Day . . . ?'

'Should be most interesting, sir.'

That topic lasted a few more minutes, and then the ginger-haired director casually changed the subject.

'Ever think of buying a house, Mr. Day ?'

'I'm afraid there's hardly enough money for that,' I grinned.

'Well, what about a tenancy?'

'Well—er——'

'Yes?'

'It's rather hard to explain.'

'Try,' said the grey-moustached director. 'We would like to know why you would rather be a manager than have a business of your own.'

Yes, I bet you would! thought I. But I had come prepared for that question. It had nearly floored me at a previous interview, with another firm. In fact, for all I knew, it had floored me—I was still uncertain—because my idea was to learn as much as possible about the business at someone else's expense before risking my own tiny capital; and that had been rather difficult to explain to a potential employer. This time I had planned to skate round the subject.

'Well, I've—er—managed to save a little,' I began, with what I hoped sounded like spontaneous candour. 'Not a lot, sir, you understand, but all the same I'm pretty glad now that it's not in rubber. I lost what I did put in rubber, and if I put all I have left into a public house all my eggs would be in one basket, wouldn't they?' I paused, and smiled ingenuously while that sank in.

The chairman blinked, first at the ginger-haired director, who smiled as if to say he thought my idea a splendid one; and then at the grey-moustached fellow, who nodded as if to say he thought I might be speaking the truth but it sounded a dashed silly notion to him.

'Yes—I see your point, Mr. Day,' muttered the chairman doubtfully.

'Now, what about references?'

'I'm forty now,' I smiled, pleased at getting over that bad patch so easily, 'and I've been with the same firm since I was twenty-three; different plantations, but the same firm.'

'Hm. That's good enough for us; but just at the moment it's the last seven years we're concerned with.'

'Oh. Well, I don't know what you'll do about the Army period, sir.'

'The police will look after that.'

'Eh!' cried Irene and I together.

Everyone else laughed.

'We engage you,' explained the ginger-haired director, 'but the police take up your references. Then they can tell the licensing magistrates whether you're fit to hold a licence or not.'

'Oh,' said Irene and I.

'The magistrates want references to cover the whole of the last seven years.'

'Oh,' I said again. 'Well, they'll be okay.'

'Yes,' laughed the chairman; 'but where do the police go for them? I mean the plantation ones. Out to Singapore or somewhere?'

'Oh, no, sir. The head office in Mincing Lane.'

'Do the people there know you personally?'

'Not half they don't, sir!' I grinned. 'I've planted with most of the directors. They'll be tickled to death when a policeman turns up.'

Everyone laughed, and the chairman glanced at the secretary.

'Better give him a form, Mr. Jones.'

Mr. Jones slid one across the table.

'References in paragraph seven,' he said. 'That's all we need now; I can fill in the rest from your letter.'

'Thanks,' I said; and pulling out my fountain-pen I jotted them down.

'I think that will be all for now, Mr. Day,' smiled the chairman.

'Thank you, sir,' said I, and glanced at Irene.

She stood up, and the two of us said good-bye; and a couple of minutes later we were in the street.

'Well,' I grinned, 'what d'you think of 'em, girl?'

'Better than the last bunch.'

'Mm,' I agreed. 'More maty.'

'Oh, much! They didn't think a hell of a lot of my cooking though.'

'Or my reasons for not wanting a pub of my own; especially the long thin fellow at the end.'

'No, I noticed that,' smiled Irene. 'By the way, he's the one who picks the typists.'

'Oh? How d'you know?'

'I could tell.'

'How?'

'By the way he looked at my legs.'

'Oh . . .! You couldn't tell what the wages are, could you? No one's mentioned them yet.'

'Bit early, isn't it?'

'No. Why? The others did.'

'Perhaps this lot expect us to ask.'

'Hm! Bit undignified—having to ask what your wages are. Dash it!'

'Yes. Bit shy-making too. What did you do in Malaya?'

'Gosh, girl! have you forgotten? Old Sir John gave me Bukit Melintang between chuckers at the Rajah Muda's.

Don't you remember? And old Bassett, bless his heart! fixed me up with Sungie Serimpat over a couple of stingahs at the Spotted Dog after the interstate rugger final. There's a proper routine there.'

'Yes, but these people aren't sahibs, darling. We don't meet them socially.'

'No—quite! We're up against a different caste system here. But still, they seem quite human.'

'Oh, yes—distinctly human ; except—er——'

'Except what?'

'Well, all three of them were smoking right through the interview, but no one thought of offering me a cigarette.'

'Ah! There you are! Different caste system. You probably rank with the secretary chap. He wasn't smoking. Weird, isn't it? I wonder what they thought of us.'

'They're for us, every time.'

'You think so?'

'Oh, definitely!'

'Looks like we've got a job, then.'

'Oh, I think so, darling. Odds on, I should say. But what do we do if both firms give us a job?'

'Dash out and buy ourselves lots and lots of drinks, my beautiful. Come on, let's have one now.'

'Better get away from this district first.'

'Yes, perhaps you're right. *Hi!* TAXI!'

II

IT was a lovely May morning, and in the opinion of most Londoners pleasantly warm; but to Irene and me, who had lived within five degrees of the equator, it was distinctly shivery; so I was not a little pleased when she suddenly scrambled out of her bed and skipped across the room to light the gas-fire and ring. Closing my eyes, I wondered hopefully if she would get up again and make the tea; but it was not to be. Presently she called me.

'Hoy, lump! Kettle's boiling.'

I rolled dutifully out of bed, and after saluting her more or less chastely on the lips, made the tea, and went downstairs for the newspapers. Underneath them were three letters, two for me and one for the Radleys.

The Radleys were our tenants, or rather Irene's tenants, because she owned the house. She had inherited it fully furnished only a few weeks ago; which was just the way things would happen when one of our chief reasons for wanting a pub was because it would be somewhere to live; and as it was a big house we kept the top two floors for ourselves and let the ground one as a flat.

I put the Radleys' letter and their paper on the hall table, and, opening one of my own letters, found it was headed *P. H. Kent & Co. (Licensed Caterers) Ltd.* It ran:

Regarding your application for employment, the directors will be pleased to grant you a further interview if you and your wife will attend at this office on Wednesday the 27th inst. at 11 a.m. Kindly confirm.

16

'What ho! What ho!' I dashed upstairs, let our Siamese cats Rubbertumi and Kinkiboo out of the kitchen, and hurried to the bedroom whistling a gay *Hark the Herald Angels Sing*.

'Hoy, you *orang bodoh*, for heaven's sake put a sock in it!' cried Irene. 'It's not Christmas. You'll have the Radleys complaining.'

'I should worry,' I grinned, throwing the letter on her bed. 'They can have the whole house to themselves now if they like.'

'What's this?' she snapped.

'Read it.'

The next moment she let out a yell of joy.

'Oh, Bill! Hurray! We've got a job, boy.'

'Looks like it, girl.'

'Quaint English they use, don't they?'

'*What ho! What ho!*'
I dashed upstairs

'Mm,' I said, reading the other letter. 'Gosh! Here's one from the first bunch. Listen:

'*Further to your visit of the 15th inst., we shall be glad if you will call here with your wife at 11.30 a.m. on Friday next the 29th instant.*'

'Crikey!' exclaimed Irene. 'If we go on like this we'll be able to fix all our pals with pubs. Aren't you clever! And aren't they fond of this word "further"? What's it mean?'

'Mean, you ass! Same as "farther", of course.'

'Ass yourself! What's a farther interview? I say, can't you see yourself writing to the brewers? "Farther to my order of the fourth kindly forward a farther forty firkins." A firkin is a kind of beer barrel, isn't it? Drink your tea, darling, and let's get bathed. You must answer these directly after breakfast.'

'Righto.' I toddled along to the bathroom and turned on the taps.

Presently Irene joined me; and a moment later she was stretched full length in the hot water.

'Ah!' she breathed. 'Lovely! I don't know which is the best, cold water in the tropics or hot water in England. Hope there's a decent bathroom in our pub.'

'We won't take it if there isn't,' I grinned from the shaving mirror.

'No; rather not.'

Kinkiboo was playing with the drips from the hot tap. Irene dabbed her nose with a wet toe.

'Think we'll have much trouble with servants, darling?'

'Jack Summers at the Three Kings says you can get 'em in pubs,' I told her. 'He says it's only private houses they don't like. They call themselves cleaners, or dustpan hostesses or something, of course.'

'Oh—quite! They would! Seems to me publicans are the only people who lead normal lives nowadays. I mean, with servants and cooks. Don't you think so? Beats me why more people of our class don't try it.'

'Mm. Rummy, isn't it?'

'Baffles me, old cock. Especially with no cooking to do. And in these days! Won't it be fun when we're out anywhere? I shall be able to say in a loud voice, "Oh, darling, remind me to tell Cook so and so," and everyone in sight will stop talking and stare at us. I shall feel like a duchess.'

'Yes,' I laughed. 'That's the side that appeals to me more than anything. I hate doing things myself: you know, washing dirty dishes, and cleaning my shoes. Ugh!'

'So do I, especially after the East. I'm better at planning things. I'll concentrate on the domestic staff; and if we get a good cook who is a good manager, that'll be half the battle. We'll build up a big lunch trade that way.'

'That's the idea! Then the firm will raise our screw. Who's cooking the breakfast this morning, sweetheart, you or me?'

'Er—let me see——'

'What is there?'

'Erm—I believe I forgot to get anything. Would you like sardines on toast, darling, or are you tired of them?'

'I'd rather have them on fried bread.'

'Oh. I don't think there's a lot of fat.'

'All right, have toast then; and put stacks of butter on it.'

'Hm . . . ?'

'What's up?'

'I've just remembered we're right out of butter.'

'Well, never mind, we'll have toast and jam, the same as we had yesterday; and you can do the cooking—if there's any bread.'

While Irene was scorching the toast I answered the letters; and after breakfast we went for a walk, and posted them, and did the shopping. Hardly were we back than a familiar fanfare on a motor horn told us my sister was calling.

Enid is a few years younger than I, and a widow, and according to present-day standards quite wealthy. She didn't know anything about our plans for keeping a pub, because she had been away for some time staying with her in-laws. We watched her saunter up the drive and enter the house, and then went to our little upstairs front door to greet her.

'Hallo, children,' she smiled, 'you look as if you are up to something. What's in the air?' She gave me a cheek to kiss, and patted Irene on the back. She is not fond of embracing her own sex.

'Come and sit down, and we'll tell you,' smiled Irene. 'Like a drink?'

'Mm! One of your fizzy Malay ones. It's quite hot this morning, isn't it?'

I turned out the gas-fire, and went to the kitchen for ice to make some cold gin slings.

'Bill's chucked his job,' remarked Irene.

'Oh! Then aren't you going back to Malaya?'

'No.'

'And a good thing too!' exclaimed Enid fervently. 'Malaya is no country for white women nowadays. Besides, Bill can't spend the rest of his life saving you from bandits. He'd probably get killed the next time. P'raps you too. How's his leg?'

'Still limping a bit.'

'Hm—not much good for planting.'

'No.'

'Doctor doubts if it ever will be,' said I, coming in with the ice.

'Oh. What will you do for a living?'

'Keep a pub,' smiled Irene.

'What! You two! A public house?'

'Yes. Why not?'

'No reason why not, my dear. But have you got one?'

'Not quite.'

I explained the situation.

'We've had interviews with two firms, and they've both made dates for second interviews.'

'Well, I think you're very clever, Bill. Half the people one meets nowadays seem to be trying to get a pub.'

'Are they?'

'Oh, yes; it's quite the thing, Bill. It's partly the housing shortage. You see, they get somewhere to live. But none of the people I know ever get any answers to their letters.'

'No,' I grinned. 'Neither did I at first. Then I broke away from the usual routine, and instead of asking for a pub, wrote and told them how I would run one if I got it.'

'And it worked!'

'There's the answer.' I pointed at the two letters.

'Good for you! But you aren't buying one, are you? You haven't enough money for that, surely?'

'No, we're going to be managers.'

'Oh! Do they pay well?'

'One firm hasn't mentioned money yet, but the other one suggested ten pounds. I suppose they'll pay more later on.'

'Hm—only twenty pounds a week for the two of you!'

'No; ten pounds joint salary.'

'Gracious! You must get your drinks for nothing.'

'Well, we get everything else—housing, lighting, fuel, food, servants——'

'Servants! That's a consideration, if you can get them. But twenty—I mean ten pounds a week! Couldn't you rent a place and keep all the profits to yourself?'

'I've only enough money for a tiny little one.'

'Goodness! I can lend you some.'

'Thanks, dear, but we'd rather play off our own bats.'

'Then why don't you take a tiny little place and save up for a bigger one?'

'You can't earn enough to save if it's too small. I thought I'd do better if I learnt the job first. You see, these big firms train you before they give you a managership.'

'Have you much to learn, dear? I thought you'd made a life-study of the trade.'

'Don't be rude.'

'Well, perhaps you're right. There's probably more in it than one imagines. What were they like, these people you saw?'

'Not bad; especially the second lot.'

'Did you have to "sir" them?'

'Oh, yes.'

Enid laughed.

'What a lark! Did it come naturally?'

'Fairly. I pretended I was back in the Army. That was Irene's idea.'

'She didn't "sir" them, did she?'

'Good lord, no!'

'Will you call your customers "sir"?'

'No fear! I loathe publicans who call me "sir". Takes all the fun out of the drink.'

'I quite agree; and I like barmaids who call me "dear". Well, I must go now. Thanks for the drink. What d'you call it? Gin slim?'

'Sling.'

'Oh, sling, is it? It was lovely. I'm longing to see you both behind a bar. I'll bring some pals along as soon as you're fixed. Gin sling—I must remember that. I say, what fun, Bill, if you have to sling your own sister out one night! Bye-bye, children.'

III

ON Wednesday, when we kept our appointment with Messrs. P. H. Kent and Company, we were treated like old friends of the firm.

'Good morning, Mrs. Day; good morning, Mr. Day,' smiled a typist. 'Go into the waiting-room. I'll tell Mr. Jones you're here.' She tripped down the passage.

Mr. Jones, the secretary, came in looking almost cheerful.

'Ah, there you are! I'll tell the directors you're here.' He bustled into the board-room.

'We're fixed,' whispered Irene.

I nodded.

'Looks like it.'

Mr. Jones flung open the door.

'Come in, will you?'

'Don't forget they haven't mentioned money yet,' whispered Irene nervously.

'No fear!' I grinned. 'In you go.'

More smiles and welcomes. Mr. P. H. Kent, the bald-headed managing director—we had sorted the names out from their headed notepaper by this time—beamed chubbily over the top of his glasses at us from his large chair at the middle of the table; Mr. Marnes, looking leaner and lankier than ever, grinned at us from the far end; while Mr. Jones sat down opposite Mr. P. H., and smiled inoffensively at everyone except us; and Mr. Bertram, the ginger-headed director, sitting next to the chairman again, twirled his handlebar moustache at Irene and played noughts and crosses with himself on a sheet of otherwise virgin blotting-paper.

As soon as we were settled on our old chairs at the foot of the table we were told there was a vacancy for a training couple at the Gorget Hotel in Haymarket ; also, that there would shortly be a vacancy for a managing couple, though one could not say exactly when—there was a businesslike vagueness about the proceedings, the directors obviously being old hands at engaging people—but it was hoped we would not have to wait long . . . after all, there was no set length to training periods . . . some learnt quicker than others . . . no need to explain that to present company, 'Ha-ha !'—broad beams from the directors and smirks from Irene and self—mumble-mumble-mumble . . . then, of course, when you get your house we give you an agreement . . . mumble-mumble . . . pounds a week—er—subject to termination on either side . . . three months' notice . . . all the usual clauses, 'Ahem-brup !' . . . so that's all agreed . . . now you better run along to the Gorget . . . see when they can start you . . . nice couple . . . 'Lawson' is the name . . . mumble-mumble-mumble . . . any questions ? 'No ? Right ! Good-bye.' Mr. Jones opened the door, and the next moment we were out in the street, in a sort of daze.

We stood and stared at one another.

'What did he say the wages were ?' I muttered.

'I don't know,' growled Irene. 'I'm trying to think. Didn't he say we only get half while we're training ?'

'Yes, but half what ?'

'Don't ask me,' she snapped. 'I keep on telling you I'm trying to think. Oh, you are a fool ! Don't you know what you accepted ?'

'Well, everything was over so quickly. I was outside before anything registered.'

'Gosh! Married to an imbecile! I suppose you did accept?'

'Must have done: we start training in a day or two. Think I'd better go back and ask?'

'And let them know we're a couple of half-wits! No thanks. We want to keep that to ourselves.'

'Well, what are we to do?'

'Have to wait till the end of the week, I suppose, and see what they give us.'

'Think they'll pay us weekly?'

'Oh, my gosh! Have we to wait a month before we know what our salary is? We'd better go after the other job, and find out before we accept it.'

We sauntered mournfully along the pavement towards the station.

'Let's go over the whole interview right from the beginning,' I suggested.

'Wait a minute,' said Irene; 'it's coming back to me. The first mention of pay was when Mr. Kent said they paid eight pounds, and you hiccuped and——'

'I remember,' I interrupted; 'and young Handlebar said that in our case, as I'd been a manager with my last firm—er—employment or something. . . . What did he say after that?'

'Old Chubby muttered something about half-salary while training.'

'That's right! And Marnes said five pounds didn't seem a lot, but on the other hand we were being taught a job.'

'You've got it,' laughed Irene. 'Then we must be getting ten pounds, the same as the other firm pays.'

'Thank goodness we've remembered,' I breathed. 'What a relief! Let's have a drink.'

'Yes, let's. Where shall we go? To the Lawsons?'

'Might as well.'

'D'you know where it is? Or have you forgotten that?'

'No, I wrote it down. It's in Haymarket, and it's called the Gorget Hotel. Come on, here's a Piccadilly bus. We can get off at the Circus.'

It was a pleasant pub, built in the style of some period or other which neither of us could place. Inside it seemed to be some other unplaceable period, or periods! But quite cosy. There weren't many customers about, just a sprinkling, and one barmaid who was serving someone. We went to the other end of the bar, where a man of about my own age was staring sort of sadly at his own thoughts. Presently he noticed us.

'Yes?' he yawned.

I ordered a light sherry and a double whisky, and when he reached for the spirit measure something about the way the barmaid hopped aside suggested to me that he might be the manager. Irene thought so too; so when he brought the drinks he found both of us beaming at him, all eyes and teeth, like a couple of dud comedians.

'Are you Mr. Lawson?' I beamed.

'Uh,' he replied.

'In that case,' I said, 'you'd better have something yourself. You're going to get a shock in a minute.'

'Uh?' said he, nearly smiling.

'What will you have?' I asked, still beaming.

'Drop o' Scotch.' He helped himself and gave me my change.

'Kent and Company are sending us to train under you,' I grinned.

'Oh, it's you, is it ? Head Office just rung up.' He gulped his whisky and disappeared.

Irene and I exchanged glances.

'Not very promising,' I murmured.

'Strewth !' she whispered.

'Think he's alive ?'

'Don't know, darling.'

He came back a few moments later with a broad-shouldered woman with very chestnut hair and lots of jewellery.

'There you are,' he mumbled, pointing at us.

'I'm Mrs. Lawson,' said the woman ; and a wave of scent wafted across the counter.

'Oh !—er—good morning,' said I, backing away from the smell.

'How d'you do !' breathed Irene.

Mrs. Lawson eyed us thoughtfully.

'So you're Mr. and Mrs. Day, are you ? Hmm !'

'Er—yes,' I smiled.

'I hope we won't be too much trouble,' said Irene turning on her charm.

'Oh no, I'm used to couples,' observed Mrs. Lawson ominously.

'We'll do our best to fit in,' I murmured ingratiatingly.

'That's the best way,' she sniffed. 'When are you coming ?'

'How would Monday suit ?'

'I shall be out on Monday.'

'Oh ! Well, what about Tuesday ?'

'The stocktaker is coming on Tuesday.'

'Wednesday ?'

'Yes. Come and see your room.' She raised the counter flap and swept through the saloon, leaving a wake of perfume behind her.

Irene and I followed, feeling like a couple of children arriving at a new school, and passing through a small hall, trailed behind her up two flights of stairs, trying not to giggle at her wobbling posterior and the tiny fat feet and skinny ankles that supported it.

When we reached the first landing she jerked her thumb at an open door.

'That's the staff-room,' she said.

I caught a glimpse of a broken armchair, a gas-fire surrounded by matchsticks and cigarette ends, and one half of a table covered with a tea-and-gravy-stained cloth littered with crumbs.

On the top landing she flung open a door.

'There you are.'

Peering inside, Irene and I saw a long passage-shaped attic dimly illuminated by a shaft of light from a tiny dormer window set in the sloping ceiling, and ranged along the inner wall a single bed, a chest of drawers, a chair, and another single bed, in that order. There was no fireplace, but to ensure a proper flow of fresh air an ingenious builder had fixed an iron ventilator into the wall immediately below the window. Little spirals of dust rising from the bare linoleum testified to its efficiency.

'Nice and compact,' commented Irene, innate politeness forcing her to praise something.

'Anywhere to hang things?' I asked. We are both careful with our clothes.

'There's a hook on the door,' replied Mrs. Lawson, pointing at a four-inch nail.

'Lovely!' murmured Irene.

'Bathroom is opposite,' frowned Mrs. Lawson.

We crossed the landing to inspect it, and found a dusty basin with tarnished taps, and standing on the bare boards an equally dusty bath containing a dead spider, two dead bluebottles, and a wafer of soap which ages ago had probably been white, but had now attained a rich old-ivory colour.

Irene twiddled the hot tap, and to our surprise out gushed steam and scalding water.

'Oh, good!' I exclaimed tactlessly. 'At least we'll be able to keep clean.'

'Lovely!' murmured Irene again.

Mrs. Lawson glared at us, apparently under the impression that we were unused to hot water.

'The other place is next door,' she remarked loftily.

'Thanks,' murmured Irene.

Not liking to inspect that, we followed Mrs. Lawson downstairs to the hall, whence she went straight into the saloon.

'Think we could go now?' whispered Irene.

'I've left my umbrella in there,' I replied.

'Oh.'

We found it still hanging on the counter by the remains of our drinks. By that time Mrs. Lawson was behind the counter again.

'Care for a drink?' I asked her, hoping to break the ice.

'I've just had a cup of tea.'

'Oh.' I finished mine in one gulp, and glanced at Irene.

She swallowed hers as if she were taking a dose of medicine, and turned to Mrs. Lawson.

'Well—we must be going now,' she said, glowing matily. 'I

do hope we won't be too much trouble; and thanks *so* much for showing us round. We'll do our best to fit in. Good-bye. See you on Wednesday.'

Ever the little lady, she smiled sweetly, and passed into the street. Endeavouring to emulate her good manners, I politely raised my hat—which always makes me feel silly in a pub—and started to follow her.

'Mr. Day!'

I turned back.

'Yes, Mrs. Lawson?'

'You'll find the side door on the latch on Wednesday. You can go straight up to your room.'

'Oh, thank you!'

'I'll expect you in the saloon at five. We open at half past.'

'Right you are.' I raised my hat again; but she had turned away, so hastily pretending I was only adjusting its angle, I hurried after Irene.

She was walking slowly down the street frowning at the pavement when I joined her.

'I suppose, *really*,' she remarked in a small voice, 'there are no proper arrangements for trainees.'

'I suppose, *really*, there aren't,' said I, thinking she had put the case in a nutshell. 'D'you think you'll be able to stick that old cow?'

'Let's hope it won't be for long. Think you can stand Lawson?'

'Oh, he's all right; he just doesn't know he's alive. I'm thinking about you. Ma is the boss.'

'Don't worry about me, boy. I shan't let that scented popsey get me down.'

'That's the spirit!' I cried. 'Gosh, that scent! Didn't it stink! We can have a smack at the other job if you like.'

'No ; I don't like them.'

'Or I can write some more letters. We're only down to K in the directory. There's over half the alphabet left yet.'

'That would mean more interviews. No. I can't stand those interviews ; they give me an inferiority complex.'

'Do they ! They don't me.'

'It's different for you : you're a man ; but I'm not used to men smoking and not offering me a cigarette, and remaining seated when I get up to go. It makes me feel like some little scullery maid. No ; now we've got this far we'll go here.'

'Okay. As long as you can stick the old cow.'

'Oh, don't worry about her ! Or him. As a matter of fact, those two have given me confidence.'

'Oh, have they ! How ?'

'Darling, if a couple of nitwits like them can run a pub, you and I could run the blooming Ritz.'

IV

IT was Wednesday afternoon. Irene and I had unpacked our suitcases and were waiting in the hall outside the saloon, thinking sadly of Rubbertumi and Kinkiboo who had been put in a cattery the previous day.

'Think they'll be warm enough?' wondered Irene. 'I mean, after Malaya and our cosy flat.'

'Oh, yes. It's summer. They'll keep each other warm.'

'All the same, I wish Enid could have had them.'

'Much better off in a cattery; that Rover of hers is a one-cat dog.' I comforted her with a little kiss on the back of her neck. 'Isn't it five yet?'

'Ten past. Oh, here they are.'

Mrs. Lawson could be heard crossing the landing at the top of the stairs.

'They're here, Ted,' she shouted. 'You show Mr. Day the pumps, and I'll show Mrs. Day the snacks.'

'Uh,' grunted Mr. Lawson; and following her down, he unlocked the saloon and went in. We noticed that he went in before his wife, but she didn't seem to mind. 'Ever work a beer ingine?' he asked me. 'It's quite easy.' Without waiting for an answer he drew up half a pint of mild ale and poured it into a drip can. 'Think you can do that?'

'Yes,' I smiled.

'Right. Don't do anything tonight. Just watch. That's the way to learn. See?'

'Yes.'

'Okay. If you want to smoke you'd better do it now; you

ain't allowed to when we're open. If you want to smoke then, you go down in the cellar. See?'

'Yes,' I said, pulling out my cigarette-case. 'Where is the cellar? Cigarette?'

'Thanks. Want to see it?'

'Yes, please.'

He led the way into the public bar and lifted a trapdoor and, after pressing down an electric switch, slithered down a ladder, followed by myself.

Pausing at the bottom to look round, I saw rows of barrels ranged on long wooden stands against white-washed walls, with here and there a rubber-jointed glass tube leading from a barrel to a hole in the ceiling—all rather as I had expected. Cases of bottled beer were stacked in towering piles in the middle of a cement floor. At the far end there was a shoot leading down from the street, and near it a sink with hot and cold taps; and beside the ladder, a small lift for sending bottled goods up to the bars.

'Whenever you see me come down here,' said Mr. Lawson, 'you want to come down and watch. That's better than being told.'

'Righto,' I nodded. 'And do I do the same when the cellarman comes down?'

'There ain't no cellarman. I sacked him when I heard you was coming. You want to learn, don't you?' His face cracked into a faint smile.

'Oh, yes—quite!' I grinned appreciatively. I was glad that at least one of the Lawsons had a sense of humour.

'Know anything about beer?' he asked.

'Only how to drink it,' I smiled.

His face nearly cracked again.

'Just watch me,' he said, 'and you'll soon learn. I been in

this line all me life.' He led the way upstairs, and then wandered gloomily round the building unlocking and opening grids and doors, but leaving the grids half drawn. Then he went back to the saloon, where Mrs. Lawson was still showing Irene the snacks.

'Be careful,' I heard her say, 'and don't get the glass cloths mixed up with the tea cloths, because the grease stops the beer frothing. And keep everything clean—spotless. We have a reputation for cleanliness.' At that moment she bumped a tray of pies to the floor with her elbow. 'Tch!'

Irene put the tray back on the counter.

'No, not there!' cried Mrs. Lawson, returning it to the floor. 'People can see in from the street.'

Irene helped to collect the pies; and observing Mrs. Lawson blow meticulously on each one before putting it back on the tray, she did the same.

'That's right,' said Mrs. Lawson; 'and you'd better give them a wipe over when you get time. I like everything spotless. Now take your pencil and paper and I'll give you the rest of the prices. This is veal-and-ham loaf, and it's six-pence a slice. That's Melton Mowbray: tenpence a slice.'

'Oh!' exclaimed Irene. 'I thought those were both the same.'

'No; if you look carefully you'll see they're a slightly different shape,' said Mrs. Lawson without any intention of being funny.

'I see. Square, sixpence; nearly square, tenpence,' muttered Irene, peering to see if that was the only difference. She didn't like to ask.

'And when you cut them don't touch them with your fingers. Push the slice on to the plate with a knife.'

'Righto; but I'll have to hold the pie, won't I?'

'Naturally,' snapped Mrs. Lawson; 'but don't touch the slice. That's never done in good-class houses.'

'Oh!' said Irene. She had often wondered why waiters were so fond of juggling rolls with spoons. Apparently this was the explanation. It was the thing! She made a mental note: Touch to cut but not to putt.

'You can do what you like under the counter, of course,' remarked Mrs. Lawson reasonably.

'Oh, of course!' said Irene intelligently.

'I suppose you know how to use a cash register?'

'No, haven't the foggiest.'

'Good lord!' exclaimed Mrs. Lawson. 'What work are you used to?'

'Well, I've never really done anything,' replied Irene tactlessly, 'except drive an ambulance during the war.'

'Phew! You are green, aren't you! And is your husband the same? Ted, have you shown Mr. Day the till?'

'No.'

'Well, show him while I'm showing Mrs. Day how to pull up the beer.'

Mr. Lawson and I gravitated together at the till.

'You just press the amounts what's on the keys,' he explained lucidly, 'and keep your cash separate; and keep your hands off that key what's marked "No Sale". That's for me and the missis.' He turned to his wife. 'I'll go and fetch the spirits now, dear.'

Mrs. Lawson sighed and glanced at the clock. It was obvious that hers were the brains of the establishment. She turned to Irene and me.

'Don't either of you touch anything this evening. Just watch and pick up what you can. Now I'll show you the measures. This is a single, and that's a double. And when you're serving spirits always pour them out over this grating in case some gets spilt. Don't forget that, because of the stocks.'

'Stocks . . .?' said I, puzzled.

'Yes, stocks. You can't afford to waste spirits, the way they're taxed nowadays. There's a tray under the grating, and then it goes into the ready-made cocktails for the young girls on Saturday nights.'

'What!' I gasped. 'Whisky? Gin? Rum? All mixed up together!'

'Yes; they don't know what they're drinking, those young girls. They think gin-and-mixed, and *ginanit*, as they call it, are vintage wines. And another thing, when you're serving gin mixed with something else, always put the gin in last. Understand? First the lime, or orange or whatever it is, then the gin.'

'Yes,' said Irene. 'But why is that?'

Mrs. Lawson looked at her as if she were half-witted.

'So that they can't see how much you put in, of course.'

'But you use the measure, don't you?' I inquired naively.

Mrs. Lawson sighed.

'Look, Mr. and Mrs. Day,' she said patiently, 'this is a business—and you've got to watch your stocks. When you're serving spirits with something else it gives you a chance to save a bit; so you only give three-quarters of a measure, see? Only half if they've already had three or four. That's an old custom. It's recognized in the line. It gives you a margin to play with if—er—if you get dishonest staff.'

'Suppose someone starts grumbling about short measure?' I asked.

'It's not short measure,' she snapped. 'It's an old custom;

besides, they don't see, if you know your job. You must always be watching your stocks. You'll soon find that out when you get your own house. My stocks are always right. Always. And it will look very funny if they suddenly go wrong just when you two have come here, won't it?' She gave me a hard look.

I had a feeling that she thought I was less trustworthy than Irene.

'Very funny indeed,' I muttered snottily.

She smiled, evidently under the impression that she had gained her point; and Irene and I exchanged glances behind her back.

'There's a list of liquor prices on that pad by the till,' she continued. 'You can both learn them this evening. That's all for now.'

We pored over the list, and noticed that some drinks had two prices.

'Perhaps they're for different bars,' suggested Irene. 'I'll go and ask her.' She took the list to Mrs. Lawson.

'No,' she said. 'Those are all for this bar. The low prices are for evening customers. They're mostly regulars, who live in the West End, and this is their local; but in the mornings we get all sorts of people, business men and so forth. Naturally we charge them a bit extra.'

'I see,' said Irene, and thought that over. 'But don't some people come in the morning *and* in the evening?'

'A few do,' admitted Mrs. Lawson. 'You charge them evening prices, of course, whenever they come. Everyone who comes in the evening is an evening customer, even in the morning.'

'Oh . . .!' said Irene. 'Then we have to remember which customers come both mornings and evenings?'

'Naturally! You have to know your customers; and then there are the people from the brewery, and from Head Office, and of course the directors—for heaven's sake don't forget the directors! All those people only come in the morning, but naturally you charge them evening prices.'

'Oh—I see,' said Irene thoughtfully.

'And we generally get a theatre rush about nine,' continued Mrs. Lawson. 'You charge them morning prices, of course.'

'Naturally!' cried Irene, beginning to get the hang of things. She came back to me. 'I say, cocky, there's more in this public-house business than meets the eye. You have to have a memory like an elephant. The higher prices are for theatre crowds, and *customers who only come in the mornings*; the lower ones are for everyone else, whenever they come.'

'Hm—that's interesting,' said I, frowning. 'And the directors, I take it, come under the last heading?'

'Naturally,' smiled Irene. 'They pay evening prices.'

'Makes you think, doesn't it?'

'Yes, darling, but I've done my thinking; so don't trouble to point out that the surplus goes into Ma and Pa Lawson's pockets. I can see that for myself. Remember you're not a *tuan* in Malaya now; so pack up your old-school-tie conscience and do as you're told, like you did in the Army. We're here to learn a job.'

'Yes, but I don't like it, girl.'

'Nor do I; and when we've got our own house we won't do it; also, we'll give full measure and pinch all the trade. In the meantime, we snap into it and learn.' Irene, it seemed, had a simple philosophy hitherto unsuspected by me. She didn't believe in being harmed in the slightest degree by the dishonesty of other people; and I gathered that, if we were to work as a team, the sooner I realized it the better.

At half past five the house opened, and customers came dribbling in. By six o'clock the bars were fairly full, and by half past six Irene and I were so bored with doing nothing but watch that we were almost asleep on our feet. Then Mr. Lawson absentmindedly pushed a pound note into Irene's hand.

'Ring up five and sevenpence ha'penny and bring me the change, dear,' he said.

Irene's eyes lit up. Here was work! How lovely! She felt like a real barmaid. She bustled to the till and found the five shilling and the sevenpenny keys, and crashed them down. The drawer shot out and smacked her in the midriff.

'Ugh!' She would have to watch that in future. She found the ha'penny key, and tried to crash that down, but it wouldn't move. Rummy! The others went down all right. Oh, they were still down! She tried to pull them up. They wouldn't come. Well, never mind, the drawer was open; she could take the change, and fix that later. Now, what was it? A ha'penny from a penny was a ha'penny, and carry one. Eight from twelve—fourpence. Five from twenty—fifteen. *Fifteen and fourpence ha'penny!* She took five shillings and fourpence ha'penny from the drawer, exchanged the pound note for a ten-shilling one, and fluttered excitedly back to Mr. Lawson. 'Here you are!'

'Thanks, dear. Hey! This is a bob too much.'

'Is it!' A ha'penny from one is a ha'penny, and carry one. Eight from twelve—fourpence, carry one. Six from twenty—sixteen. No, fifteen. No, *fourteen!* 'Yes, you're quite right, Mr. Lawson. I'll put it back. By the way, the till's stuck.'

Mr. Lawson said a naughty word.

Irene flushed, but forgave him because he had not been cross with her about the shilling; and following him to the till she watched him give it a bang with the palm of his hand, and saw the jammed keys flip back into their places.

'Now I must ring up the ha'penny,' she said, striking the key with a daintily manicured forefinger; but its pointed nail skidded on to the next one. 'Oh! I've rung up three-farthings.'

'Can't you press one key at a time?'

'Yes, and jammed the blooming thing again,' growled Mr. Lawson. 'Can't you press one key at a time?'

'Sorry; my finger slipped. But I thought you pressed them all at once.'

'Yes, but I do 'em all at once.'

'Oh, I see,' said Irene, completely mystified. 'Perhaps I'd better watch a bit more.'

'Uh,' said Mr. Lawson.

'I'm sorry.'

'All ri',' said Mr. Lawson, nearly smiling.

Irene glued herself to the till and watched with pathetic concentration every time it was used, until at last she felt she knew enough to risk another try ; then the next time the barmaid came along she asked if she might work it for her.

'Yes, dear,' said the barmaid. 'Four and six it is. Put one finger on each key, and press them both down together—or else they'll jam.'

Ching !

'I've done it !' Four and six from six shillings is one and six. 'Here you are.' She tripped along to Mr. Lawson. 'May I serve someone now ?'

'Uh.'

A young man and his girl were just coming in, and she hurried to greet them.

'Good evening !'

'Good evening, miss. Brown ale and a gin-and-lime, please.'

She took a bottle of brown ale from the shelf and looked up the price, and then using both hands and the maximum amount of unnecessary strength, mangled off the crown cork—nearly dropping the bottle into the basket under the patent opener at the same time, to the audible amusement of several customers who were watching her every movement—and then with trembling fingers dribbled the ale into a carefully canted glass, as she had seen the barmaid do. Now for the gin-and-lime. She looked up the price, poured out the lime-juice, and then turned to the spirit stand—and paused. Oh ! She couldn't give that nice girl short measure ! She could see her in the mirror behind the bottles. Such an attractive girl ! And the boy only looked about twenty-two. They couldn't have been engaged long and he didn't look too well off either. Only drinking

brown ale himself, bless his heart! What a shame! Oh,
damn!—Ma Lawson was looking. Well, here goes. She
partially filled the measure. Hm . . .? Didn't look much.
And such a sweet girl too! And she looked so proud of her
boy. Better give her a tiny spot more. Oh, blast, it's running
over into the grid! Well, that's that! She emptied the
brimming measure into the lime-juice.

After that she decided to continue serving; and I thought
I would do some work too; and the time began to pass quite
pleasantly for both of us. Seeing a man fidgeting in a bored
manner with a glass of beer, I went along to cheer him up.

'That a Loamshire tie you're wearing?' I asked.

'Oh, d'you know 'em?' he smiled.

'Rather! Your second battalion was next to us at
Caen.'

'No! My dear fellow!'

The next moment the two of us were 'remembering' as
hard as we could go.

Presently another man wearing a Loamshire tie came in,
and he had a girl with him; and the first man hailed the
two of them and called for drinks. The girl didn't know
what to have, and one of the men suggested a gin-and-
orange.

'Is that nice?' she asked.

'Lovely,' said I, doing my stuff.

'All right, then, I'll have that, thank you.'

I went to the spirit stand. Heck! I couldn't give these
people short measure. Dash it, the chaps were old comrades-
in-arms; we'd fought in the same battle together. Blast!
The old cow was watching. Better get it over quickly. I
tipped three-quarters of a measure of gin into some orange
squash and put it on the counter. When I brought the

change the girl was tasting it. Presently she smelt it, and took a proper sip.

'Hasn't orange squash a strong flavour?' she remarked naively. 'You can hardly taste the gin.'

I flushed and bolted for the cellar.

'That's the last ruddy time!' I muttered as I slithered down the ladder.

'What's up?' inquired Mr. Lawson looking up from a barrel.

'Oh,' I said, 'I didn't know you were here. Nothing much. What are you doing? Tapping a barrel?'

'Uh.'

I watched the operation, and then went up and stationed myself as far as possible from the Loamshire party; and presently Irene came along and said Mrs. Lawson had told her we could go to supper.

'We have ours at the lunch counter in the lounge,' she added.

'Thank goodness for that,' I said. 'Come along, I'm going to have a drink with mine, and to hell with everybody. What do you fancy, sweetheart?'

'Guinness, please. I'll do the ordering while you get it.'

On second thoughts she decided to let me choose my own supper; and for herself ordered a slice each of veal-and-ham loaf and Melton Mowbray pie, because she wanted to find out the difference between them; and to her surprise the snack girl gave her a nasty look. When I came along with the drinks I said I would have the same; and I collected a nasty look too.

'She did that to me,' whispered Irene.

'Oh?' said I.

We were both wondering what it was all about when a

man came to the counter and asked for a slice of Melton
Mowbray pie; and he was given veal-and-ham loaf and
charged the Melton Mowbray price. So that was the
answer! We exchanged winks.

'Another old custom,' I whispered. 'And I've just discovered another one.' Then I related the following incident.

When I bought our drinks I bought one for the barmaid
as well; and she had a double gin, the same as I did, but
only charged me for two singles. So I showed her the change
she had given me, and said, 'Hoy, dear, these are doubles,
aren't they?' And all she did was to wink her eye and say,
'And how!'

'Lovely!' laughed Irene. 'And what did you do then?
Leave it at that?'

'Well—yes, I did,' I had to admit. After all, it was rather
an awkward situation; but in fairness to myself I pointed
out that the Lawsons were doing much the same themselves.

'Quite, boy, quite!' muttered Irene sagely. 'Like master
like servant. By the way, can you tell the difference between
veal-and-ham loaf and Melton Mowbray?'

'All I can taste is mustard,' I said.

After supper we went back to the saloon and served for
the rest of the evening. At closing time Irene said her feet
were aching. Mine were too, and my wound was throbbing.
We had been standing for five hours by then; and we were
not used to it.

'We'll have a drink,' I said. 'It's good for tired feet. Mind
if we have one, Mr. Lawson?'

Mr. Lawson signified with a grunt that he thought the
request a reasonable one, but looked disappointed when I
bought drinks only for Irene and myself.

After that we thought we needed some fresh air, and

went out and wandered in the streets behind Piccadilly. Neither of us had ever been in the West End at that time of night before, except by car to the theatre, or along the main roads, and it seemed to us almost like a different town; it was so quiet and peaceful after the noises of the day. Our heels echoed on the empty pavements; and for the first time we realized that off the main roads London was quite a city of trees. In the squares we looked up into expanses of open sky. We thought it rather fun; and I asked Irene if she didn't think it rather fun working together; and she slipped an arm as far as it would go round my waist, and I kissed her on the lips, and she laughed; and we went back to our little attic hand in hand like an engaged couple.

V

THE next day Mrs. Lawson lent Irene a long linen coat to wear instead of her frock, and initiated her into the mysteries of the hot-plate. The hot-plate was a huge oven with a flat top dented here and there to take joints of meat and so forth; metal covers over the dents were raised and lowered by means of chain pullies attached to the ceiling. It was some eight feet long by about four feet wide and nearly filled the service-room, which was a little Black Hole of Calcutta ventilated by a service hatch and a door that was always kept shut to segregate the smells. It was very hot, with just space for two people to work; and it was in there that Irene discovered that Mrs. Lawson put scent on her underclothes. She told me a *pot-pourri* of Brussels sprouts, Californian poppy and perspiration had to be smelt to be believed; and when I caught a whiff of her hair while kissing her good-night I quite agreed. The next day she wore a head scarf; but we never really got away from Mrs. Lawson's aura all the time we were there.

Joints, Irene discovered, were roasted the day before and allowed to harden overnight in the frigidaire. It was then possible, with a razor-sharp knife, to shave from them the thinnest of slices and cover the maximum area of plate with the minimum of meat. The plates were then put inside the hot-plate and the shavings allowed to warm, their final heating taking place when half a cupful of hot gravy was poured over them immediately before service. Irene was not allowed to carve because Mrs. Lawson had to think of her stocks.

'You can watch me, and practise when you get your own house,' said Mrs. Lawson. 'That's the way I had to learn.'

After Mrs. Lawson had arranged the meat to best advantage on the plates it was Irene's duty to add the gravy, and to apportion, in little dishes for each person, two boiled potatoes, one roast potato, and a spoonful of cabbage or four Brussels sprouts. Cherry pie was one square of pastry, eight stewed cherries, and a cupful of custard. And so on.

One day Irene put nine cherries on a plate instead of eight, but never again.

'Good heavens, you'll ruin me! Don't you ever think of my stocks? You won't behave like this when you get your own house. D'you know what those cherries cost? Can't you count?'

'All right, all right, all right! They're only small ones.'

'They're *not* small. Look at *that* one! Eight I . . .'

Meanwhile I was being taught cellar work, if one could call it being taught; because the only way I could acquire any knowledge at all, other than by watching, was by a process of question and grunt: 'uh' from Mr. Lawson doing duty for an affirmative answer, and 'uh' with a slightly different intonation—say 'uhh'—for a negative one. In this way I learnt the following:

Draught beers were of two kinds, fined and bright. Fined beer had a sediment and was temperamental, and after delivery had to be allowed to settle for forty-eight hours, and even then a slight jar would sometimes turn it cloudy; and it was affected by temperature. But bright beer had no sediment, and could be skidded off the dray, and man-handled on to the stillion—a kind of wooden cradle or

stand—and served straight away. (At the Gorget Hotel all
the bitter beer was fined, and all the mild ale was bright.)
The difference between beer and ale lay solely in the
strength, ale being merely a kind of weak beer; unless it
happened to be strong ale, when, of course, it was a kind of
strong beer. I am only repeating what he told me. Bright
beer, he said, was brewed primarily for use at sports
meetings, agricultural shows and so forth, where it was
required for consumption immediately after delivery; but
mild ale, that sweet innocuous fluid so beloved by the
British working man, was always bright.

'And a good job too!' he grunted.

'Oh? Why?' I asked.

'Because you can't put nothing back into the bitter,' he
explained with his usual lucidity.

That interested me, and eventually, by means of the
question and grunt process, I discovered that if waste beer
were put into fined beer it turned it cloudy, but that a
reasonable amount did no harm to bright beer. It must not
be imagined that all the above information was imparted to
me in one session, or even in one week; but one thing I did
learn very quickly, and without any questioning, was that
all beer collected in drip cans was invariably poured into the
mild ale, and not, as I had naively imagined, thrown away,
or even returned to the brewery as ullage as so many people
think. And at the Gorget Hotel the same was done with the
filtered dregs from barrels of fined beers, and the lees of
bottled beers and used glasses. It did not matter to Mr.
Lawson what kind of beer it was: bitter beer, light ale,
brown ale, Burton: according to him it was all fit to go into
the ale. His theme song in the matter of 'waste' was *Bung It
All into the Ale*. In other words, there was no waste.

'But don't put nothing back into the bitter,' he warned me. 'We got a very good name for our bitter.'

'Oh, lovely!' I cried. 'But don't people ever notice the ale?'

'Uhh!' he sneered (meaning 'no', of course). 'Mild-ale drinkers never notice nothing—not if you don't overdo it; and that reminds me: when you was pulling up mild-and-bitters last night I see you giving 'em half-and-half. That's no good. All you want is a drop o' bitter at the bottom o' the glass and fill up with mild. Mild's cheaper than bitter. See? You got to watch the stocks.'

'Yes,' I said; 'but I have heard customers ask which is the mild and which is the mild-and-bitter.'

'S'right,' he grinned. 'They don't know.'

There didn't seem much more to be said on that point. I nodded at a sort of china bucket that hung from a hook in the ceiling.

'What's that thing?'

'A utilizer. We call it a ute. Goes up to the mild ale in the public.'

'What's it for?'

'Why, to utilize, o' course.'

'Er—quite; but what?'

'Eh?'

Eventually I found that waste beer from the various bars drained into the utilizer, whence it was sucked into the public bar by a little auxiliary pump on the beer engine at the rate of about a spoonful per glass; but it took Mr. Lawson quite a long time to explain all that; and anyway, Mr. Lawson didn't think a lot of the thing. In his opinion it was only something extra to clean. He thought it far better to pour the stuff straight into a barrel, and be done with it.

Unfortunately, however, the directors, who were of an economical turn of mind, but mistrusted the judgment of their managers in the matter of pouring into barrels, thought otherwise ; so he told me it would be my duty every Monday morning—the day on which directors inspected the house—to pour a few pints of nice fresh ale into the thing in case one of the old baskets poked his nose into it. That pleased everybody.

VI

OUR first three weeks passed in a flash. By then we felt we had been working in a public house all our lives. We had learnt a lot more even than we thought there was to learn; though actually we had not been taught much. We were never allowed, for example, to cash-up at the end of the day, or to see any of the books; probably, we imagined, because there was some hanky-panky going on. In fact, that was pretty obvious. All the Lawsons taught us were the duties they found irksome themselves. Not that we minded carrying out those duties. The more we did the more we learnt; and if Mrs. Lawson had not loathed us so much for speaking good English—which, of course, we could not help—and because customers frequently mistook us for the governor and his wife—which we couldn't help either—we would have been very happy; and it would have been nicer too if Mrs. Lawson had not been so conscious of the fact that her hair was dyed chestnut, whereas Irene's was naturally that colour. Mrs. Lawson, it will be gathered, was one of those publicans' wives who hated pretty barmaids; and her male customers found Irene, at the age of thirty, very easy on the eye. Mr. Lawson, on the other hand, hardly ever noticed Irene, or me. He just mooned around in some animal world of his own, gazing into space and knocking back double whiskies whenever his wife turned her head. Both of them, as we gained in efficiency, took less notice of us, so by now we had made our own routines and become a part of the establishment; which pleased us immensely.

Then one evening a car drew up outside the saloon entrance, and we heard a familiar fanfare, and in breezed Enid.

'Hallo, seen Mrs. Day anywhere?' she asked Mrs. Lawson airily.

Mrs. Lawson glared—as if to say : That's not the way for a learner's friend to talk to the manageress !

'I b-beg your pardon !' she spluttered frigidly. 'Mrs. Day is——'

But Enid had seen Irene.

'Oh, there you are !' she interrupted, with a half-smile at Mrs. Lawson by way of apology. 'How are you getting on ? D'you like it ? I'm simply gasping for a drink. You'd better have one too.' She turned to Mrs. Lawson. 'Two whiskies, please.'

'Not for me, Enid,' said Irene quickly. 'We're not supposed to drink.'

'Aren't you ! What an extraordinary arrangement when you've got it all round you ! Well, I am.' She smiled at Mrs. Lawson. 'You may bring me one.' Then noticing that lady's chilly air for the first time, she looked her up and down, and turned back to Irene. 'Is that the—er—rum . . . ?' she whispered.

Irene nodded.

Enid turned her face away from Mrs. Lawson.

'Having a bit of a time, aren't you, dear ?' she muttered out of one side of her mouth. Then she sniffed—sniff-sniff ! 'What scent is she using ? Well, never mind that, where's Bill ?'

'In the public bar.'

'Where's that ?'

'At the back here.'

'I've never been in a public bar. May I go through ? I'll be back in a minute.' Enid started to raise the flap.

Mrs. Lawson rocked on her foundations.

'No-no !' said Irene hastily. 'Go round by the street. First door on the left.'

'All right. I'll be back presently.' Enid went out followed by admiring glances from all the men over twenty-five, said 'Now-now, officer, I'm just going, and you can put that notebook away,' to a policeman who was quizzing her car, and turned into the public bar. 'Oh, there you are, Bill ! How are you getting on ? Is it too awful here ?'

'Oh, not so bad. How are you ?'

'Fine, thanks. I've just ordered a whisky from that fat woman in the other bar there. Tell her to bring it in here, will you ?'

'I'll get it.' I turned, and encountered the empurpled visage and glaring eyes of our outraged manageress. 'Oh ! Er—ahem !' No—I couldn't face it. I turned back to Enid. 'Better forget it, dear. Have one with me.'

'Oh—er—all right,' she said, looking slightly puzzled ; for she had missed the by-play ; not that it would have meant much to her if she had seen it. 'Just as you like,' she muttered plaintively. 'Can't you have one too ?'

' 'Fraid not.' I gave her a whisky and a cigarette, and we chatted of this and that.

Presently she threw her cigarette away half smoked.

'It's not much fun drinking on my own. There's that woman glaring at me again. She keeps on. What's the matter with her ?' She turned her back, and Mrs. Lawson disappeared. 'I think I'll go, Bill, if you don't mind, and come and see you when you've got a pub of your own. Is she always like that, that fat woman ?'

I laughed and shrugged my shoulders. Enid grimaced.

'Like that, is it? What's her husband like?'

'Just a blob.'

'Ha! I expect that's the trouble. Well, I'm off. Say good-bye to Irene for me. I can't face that gorgon again.'

'Righto. Good-bye, dear.'

'Bye-bye. Let me know when you get a day off, and we'll all go to a show or something.'

'Right you are!'

Enid went home; and that was the turning point of our career at the Gorget Hotel. From then on Irene and I could do no right. Whether Mrs. Lawson had heard herself called 'that fat woman' or not we shall never know, but she was obviously upset by Enid's airy manner and lack of deference to the manageress of a West End licensed house. Also, she had been to the door and had a good look at Enid's car, which, it must be admitted, was somewhat noticeable. Enid's husband had been one of those successful business men who think up money-making schemes in their sleep and put them into execution the next morning over half a dozen telephones, and her car looked just like that. Henceforth Mrs. Lawson set out to teach us that whatever our friends were like, and whoever we thought we might be, we were nobodies at the Gorget Hotel.

'You put five sprouts on that plate. No—they were not small ones. There's not enough gravy on this plate. There's too much on that. Must you take all night for your suppers? There's no need to talk to customers. Serve them. You aren't managers.' And so on, and so on.

Then there came the time when Irene was left serving alone for a long while, and the next morning was told her till was short to the tune of nine shillings and ninepence.

'That'll be the change for a pound note given for a ten-shilling one,' remarked Mrs. Lawson. 'Did you have any arguments over change yesterday?'

Like a little silly, Irene admitted to an argument, but over an alleged half-crown, not a note.

'Huh!' snorted Mrs. Lawson, shaking her shoulders up and down. 'If you can make a mistake over a half-crown you can make one over a ten-shilling note.'

'I didn't make a mistake,' said Irene. 'I was right; and, anyway, why blame me? Other people used the till.'

'You used it the longest,' snapped Mrs. Lawson.

Irene could see no point in that remark; but growing tired of the argument, she decided it would be less trouble to pay; and she fetched her bag. Tears welled in her eyes. It was so disappointing. She had worked so hard; and Bill thought she had done so well; and now this! It wasn't fair. She opened her bag and extracted a ten-shilling note.

At that moment Bill came up from the cellar.

'Hallo . . . ?' I cried. 'What's up?'

She told me; and I took charge.

'Put that note back,' I snapped, reverting to type. I felt like I did on the plantation one day when I found the *kadde karan* fiddling the toddy cash, only about ten times worse, because a man doesn't like to see his wife bullied. I glared at Lawson. 'How d'you know it was her mistake?' I rasped. 'Eh?'

He flinched at the peremptory tone, and said nothing.

I turned to his wife.

'Eh?' I snapped.

She flushed and said nothing. I turned back to her husband.

'There'll be a proper way for adjusting matters like

this, the same as in any other firm—through your daily returns.'

'That's all very fine,' he blustered, now that he saw he would get no help from his wife. 'I've been with this firm nearly twelve years, and my cash has always been right.'

That amused me.

'You must be the only manager in the country who can say that,' I grinned.

'That's as may be. Somebody has got to make it up.'

'Meaning you're responsible, eh?'

'Of course I am.'

'Very well then, if that's how you feel about it, make it up yourself; and any time you feel we should refund money, let Head Office know. We'll deal with them.'

'That's just what we will do,' fumed Mrs. Lawson. 'Ted, report it to the firm.'

'Uh,' said Mr. Lawson somewhat ashamedly, and went upstairs followed by his wife.

'That's put them in their place, cocky,' smiled Irene; 'but we shall cop it now.'

'Don't you believe it!' I grinned, getting out my rags to clean the pewter. 'They'll be as sweet as treacle for the next few days. I haven't been handling men all my life for nothing. Besides——' I broke off chuckling, as I thought of something else.

'Besides what?' she asked.

'They know now, my beautiful, that we aren't afraid of Head Office. That'll set 'em thinking. All the same, I think we could do with a change.'

'D'you mean to another house?'

'Yes. Don't you?'

'I've certainly had a basinful of these birds—anyway, of Ma Lawson.'

'Okay, leave it to me. I'll have a word with one of the directors.'

The following Monday Mr. Bertram came to inspect the house, and I waylaid him and told him we would like to broaden our experience by a change to another house.

'Sorry,' he said, twirling his handlebar moustache, 'but it would be awkward to arrange a move just now. We've got you down for one in a month's time.'

'Oh!' said I despondently. 'A month!'

'Why!' he exclaimed. 'Aren't you happy here?'

'Er—it's not that, sir,' I muttered. 'It's just—er——'

'All right,' he said, interrupting me. 'I'll see what I can do. Can't promise anything though. See you next week.'

But the next week the tall lanky director called Marnes came. He caught me alone in the cellar ; and he seemed none too pleased at the encounter.

'Where's Mr. Lawson?' he snapped.

'I don't know,' I replied shortly.

He had a good look round, grunting occasionally as if annoyed at finding nothing to grumble at, and then stood on his toes and squinted into the utilizer—into which I had just poured half a gallon of nice fresh mild ale from a newly tapped barrel.

'Hm! Hell of a lot o' waste in here. That's careless serving.'

I said nothing, but decided to put only a quart in next time.

'What did you say?' he growled.

'Nothing, sir. I didn't speak.'

'Oh. Well, you've got your move,' he said pushing a slip of paper into my hand. 'That's the address. You can go tomorrow. Sorry you haven't been happy here; but you were warned it was hard work, weren't you?'

'We haven't found it too hard, sir,' I said, flushing. 'It's only that we want a change, and—er——'

'Well, you've got your change,' he grinned unbelievingly. 'There it is. We'll see what you think of the public-house business when you've been at the Block and Anchor a few weeks.'

So you think we're soft! thought I.

'Righto, sir,' I said, forcing a smile; and as he climbed up the ladder to the ground floor I read the address:

The Block and Anchor
Basin Lane
Poplar

Crikey! The dock area! I went up to the saloon and showed it to Irene.

'Do we take it?'

'You bet!' she cried. 'The firm probably think we *can't* take it. Don't you see? They're sending us there because they're annoyed with us for asking to leave here. They think we're soft. We'll show them!'

I couldn't see Irene dishing out pints of mild-and-bitter to a lot of drunken sailors and stevedores. I explained this.

'Poo!' she said. 'I can handle anything in trousers; besides, they won't have rifles like the bandits did.'

I laughed.

'Well, we needn't take it if we don't want to. There are

plenty more firms in the directory. We're only down to K
you know.'

Irene bristled.

'And let them think we've funked it! No fear! Don't
worry about me, boy. This has got my rag out.'

'Okay, sweetheart.'

VII

WE arrived at the Block and Anchor just after six o'clock in the evening; and we soon guessed why we had been sent there. Mr. Grainger, the manager, we found, had asked for a transfer because the house was too rough for him, and his wife had threatened to pack up and go back to Mother if the transfer didn't happen pretty quickly; but the directors, who seemed sympathetically disposed towards them, were having difficulty in finding another couple—the house was as rough as all that—so they probably thought it would be a good testing-place to find out whether or not our real reason for wanting to leave the Gorget Hotel was because we found the work there too hard, and that in the meantime a man of my size would be some comfort to the Graingers. So they would be killing two birds with one stone. Afterwards, we guessed there were other reasons, but more of that later.

Mr. Grainger was a little podgy, ball-shaped man of about thirty, with black hair, and worry lines under his eyes and round his mouth, and a harassed expression. When we came in he was trying unsuccessfully not to glower at his cousin, Rosie, who was acting as a temporary barmaid. What had happened we couldn't tell, but judging by the uncontrolled giggles coming from some uncouth customers at the bar, she had probably just called him by a family pet name, which we were soon to find out was a habit of hers, and which always annoyed him intensely; though he never dared to say anything.

He was always having trouble with his relations, because

owing to shortage of staff he was continually having to call
on them for help; and as they looked on helping him as
merely gentle relaxation after real work, he had no control
over them whatever.

Rosie was no exception. She took no notice of him at all.
She was an attractive little thing, with black hair dyed gold,
one lock of which she had trained to hang over her left eye;
and when serving she had a habit of tossing this lock coyly
to one side. Customers sometimes grumbled when, with the
same movement, she coyly tossed ash from the cigarette
that always dangled from her pretty lips into their beer. One
was doing so when we approached the counter.

'Ever s-sorry,' she murmured, smiling sweetly; and good-
naturedly emptying the mug into a drip can, she refilled it,
sure in the knowledge that the disparaged liquor would
soon be pumped up again for another, or the same, customer.

Mr. Grainger groaned, and turning away pained eyes,
sighed obviously for the day when he would be managing a
house in which the barmaids valued their jobs and did as
they were told. Then seeing me towering above him from
the other side of the counter, he looked up.

'Yes, sir?'

'Are you Mr. Grainger?' I asked.

'Yes, that's me.'

'Good evening,' I smiled. 'We're Mr. and Mrs. Day.'

'Oh—oh, that's fine!' He gave me a long once-over, and
his eyes lit up. 'Good evening!' he smiled, evidently having
decided I was just the chap for Saturday nights. 'Er—good
evening, Mrs. Day. Come up and see your room. We've put
you at the top of the house because of the baby.' He came
through to the front of the counter, and unlocking a door
marked *Private,* led the way across a small hall to the foot

of some oilcloth-covered stairs, and shouted: 'Lil! Lil,
here's Mr. and Mrs. Day.' Then turning to us, he said: 'Go
up. The missis will look after you.'

Mrs. Grainger was quite different from her husband; she
was tall and statuesque, and must have weighed about
thirteen stone. She had a clear velvet-like complexion, and
no make-up, and hair the colour of dark honey, simply
arranged in a thick bob; and when she came to the kitchen
door to greet us her deep blue eyes were level with mine.
Altogether a startling creature, more like a Gainsborough
duchess than the wife of an East End publican. She spoke in
pleasant, gentle tones, marred however by a suggestion of
cockney accent. She seemed very shy.

'Oh—good evening,' she said, looking first at me and then
at Irene. Then including both of us in a timid glance, she
added: 'I haven't done your room yet. I'll take a broom up.'
Going into the kitchen, she fetched a duster and a broom,
and then led the way up another flight of oilcloth-covered
stairs to the top floor, and showed us into a large airy room
containing a double bed heaped with folded blankets and
sheets. The rest of the furniture consisted of a chest of
drawers, a dressing-table, and (as at the Gorget Hotel) a nail
in the door. There were no chairs.

'Ah!' cried Irene. 'This is a bit brighter than the Gorget.
Any chance of single beds?'

Mrs. Grainger looked shocked.

'*Single—beds!* No-o,' she said very slowly, as if she
thought there was something obscene about single beds.
'Don't you *like* a double one?'

'Not frightfully keen,' replied Irene. 'We're rather a
restless couple.'

'Oh! Oh—well—then perhaps the firm will change it.'

'Never mind,' smiled Irene. 'Perhaps we'll be too tired to notice.'

'Yes,' said Mrs. Grainger surprisingly. Then adding shyly, 'I expect you'd like something to eat,' she slipped out of the room.

I closed the door behind her and grinned at Irene.

'Looks as if I'm Peggy today.' Snatching up the broom, I started to sweep vigorously.

Irene inspected the drawers.

'Hm—no paper! Wonder if they have any old newspapers. Hi, steady with that broom, cocky; you'll suffocate us.'

'Sorry,' I grinned. 'Why don't you open the window? I say, this floor hasn't been swept for years; and they might have given us a mat for our lily-whites; that is if we're going to have lily-whites. Seen a bathroom anywhere?'

'Not a glimpse. I'll have a squint round while you're enjoying this fog of yours. Can't you sweep gently? Here, give me the broom. You go and find a bathroom and some newspapers.'

'Okay.'

I went down to Mrs. Grainger; and she gave me some old papers, and told me she would leave our supper in the oven with the door open, so that we could have it when convenient. Then she showed me the bathroom. It was littered with newly washed smalls, and toilet things.

'Oh,' I remarked, 'you and your husband use this one.'

'Yes,' she nodded; 'it's the only one. Mr. Grainger comes in to shave at eight, but I wait till we're open. We have our baths on Saturday.'

'Oh . . .?' My face fell, because we rather fancy a bath every day. I mentioned this.

'Oh, all right,' she said disbelievingly. 'I'll tell Kate. She sees to the boiler.'

'Thank you.' I turned to go, but she was standing in the doorway. 'Er—thank you very much,' I said, in a slightly louder tone, hoping she would take the hint and move out of the way.

She didn't move. She just stood there, staring at me, with her big blue eyes only a few inches from mine; and there was a twinkle of laughter in them. She was so close I became conscious of the natural scent of her hair. I began to wonder. Surely she wasn't getting coy—this great statue of a woman! I rather incline to the dainty little feminine types myself. But, dash it, seen close to she looked feminine all right. In fact, there was definitely a sort of 'something' about her; and her hair smelt nice too—even if she didn't bath very often. And after all, I mused, lots of people don't bath every day. She probably washed down or something. And those eyes of hers, they were still laughing at me. It was quite catching. I felt my own crinkling at the corners. Then my lips curved automatically into a smile.

'Er—thank you very much indeed,' I said, just to be on the safe side.

'I've got a baby,' she remarked apropos of nothing at all.

'Eh! Oh—er—how nice!' I gasped, not knowing what else to say. Well anyway, I thought, that's all right; she can't want another. Dash it! With Irene in the house, and all that, what the heck!

'Come and see him,' she ordered; and clutching my arm, she tugged me across the landing and into a bedroom.

I'm frightened to death of babies. Always have been. I don't know what to say to them. Puppies and kittens, yes; I'm all for them. And as a schoolboy, of course, I went

C

through the normal white mice and caterpillar stages. I had
even kept a grass snake. But babies, no. They make me
nervous.

'Oh—er—rer . . .' I said, timidly propping the door open
for the sake of the conventions.

'Come on,' she said, and pulling me to the far side of the
room, showed me a baby boy lying on his back in a pram.

He was a nice little chap, not a bit like his father, and as
masculine as they make them; and gurgling away to beat
the band. But Mother seemed to be waiting for the polite
paeans of praise.

'By Jove! Jolly little beggar, what! How old is he?'

'Thirteen months.'

'Is that all!' I exclaimed, rather cleverly I thought.
'What's his name?'

'Prebern.'

'Eh!'

'Prebern.'

'How d'you spell it?'

'P, r, e, b, e, r, n.'

'Go on!' I said. 'Are you sure?'

'Well, how would you spell it?'

'I mean—are you sure it's his name?'

'Of course! I gave it to him.'

'Well, I'm blowed!' I exclaimed.

'You may play with him sometimes,' she said.

'Th-thank you,' I replied nervously. 'Er—I must be going
now'; and hurrying from the room, I ran upstairs, to find
Irene had finished sweeping the floor and started to unpack.

'Where've you been all this time?' she asked. 'Coying
with Lil?'

'No, I don't think so.'

'What d'you mean—you **don't** think so! Don't you know when you've been coying?'

'I never coy,' I grinned. 'But, d'you know, I thought that bit was shy when I first saw her.'

'If by "that bit" you mean Mrs. Grainger I still think she's shy,' smiled Irene, fitting some paper into a drawer.

'Hmm—I dunno. She's got a baby.'

'Well, shy women can have babies, can't they! It's quite respectable, you know, if they're married.'

'Yes, but this poor little swine is called Prebern.'

'Called *how much*?'

'Prebern. P, r, e, b, e, r, n. Prebern.'

'What on earth for!'

'Don't ask me.'

'But is that a name?'

'Well, she knows how to spell it.'

'Boy or girl?'

'Boy. Nice little chap too; simply oozing sex.'

'Oh, you've seen it! Hope he doesn't take after his father, poor little thing!'

'I don't think so—or his mother; but he did remind me of somebody. By Jove! I've got it: he's the dead spit of old Marnes.'

'Marnes? D'you mean Mr. Barnes, the butcher?'

'No, you idiot—our director. Marnes. The one you said picked the typists.'

'Oh, nonsense!'

'He is,' I laughed. 'D'you think we've stumbled on something?'

'I say, what a lark if we have! She's a fascinating piece, you know.'

'D'you think so?'

'Well, don't you? With some good clothes and a touch of make-up she'd be a riot, man.'

'Bit monumental for my taste; but she certainly has something.'

'Something! I bet many a film star started with half what she has. All she lacks is brain. Think we ought to go down and do some work?'

'Perhaps we'd better. I'll have a recce while you finish unpacking.'

I tripped downstairs, whistling a slight tune, and feeling how nice it was to be away from the Gorget Hotel, and reaching the next floor, heard Mrs. Grainger shout my name from the kitchen.

Hmm . . .? I wondered, and peeped cautiously inside; but it was all right: she only wanted to show me where the things were kept.

'Look,' she said, 'that's the boiler for the hot water, in the corner there. Kate looks after it; but she generally forgets, so it's better to do it yourself when you want a bath; and— er—she fetches the coke. That's kept in the yard, if you—er —if she—er—that is——'

'I understand,' I said.

'Mr. Grainger will show you where it is,' she smiled. 'I never go downstairs myself, except to clear up after we're closed.'

'Oh? How's that?' I asked.

'I don't like it,' she replied.

'Oh, what a shame!' I exclaimed, thinking that a somewhat peculiar statement to come from a publican's wife.

'I'd rather have my cake shop,' she muttered.

I began to wonder if she were a bit touched.

'Oh, naturally!' I agreed, trying to look understanding,

and wondering what on earth she was talking about. 'Absolutely! Every time!'

'The knives and forks are in here,' she smiled, opening a drawer in the table, 'and there's a tablecloth at the back. You can lay your own table, can't you?'

'In here?' I asked.

'Yes.' She shut the drawer, and came and stood quite close to me, and laughed at me with her eyes as she had done in the bathroom doorway. 'Going downstairs now?' she asked unexpectedly.

'Yes, I suppose I'd better,' I replied.

'All right,' she said, still more unexpectedly. 'You may play with Prebern when you want to.'

'Thank you,' I murmured gravely, and backing awkwardly from the room, went downstairs feeling rather like Gulliver must have felt after conversing with a child giant in the fabulous land of Brobdingnag.

VIII

When I went into the saloon Mr. Grainger told me he was just going down into the cellar.

'You'd better come with me,' he added.

I followed him down a flight of stone steps, and came to a large badly lighted cellar, and pausing to look round, was amazed at its dirty condition. Everything was dusty, and the floor littered with crown corks, broken cases, smashed bottles, and discarded broom-heads. The felt bag for filtering the dregs from bitter-beer barrels smelt like sour cheese. The brass dipstick and the copper funnels were green with verdigris, buckets were ringed with dried froth. I had never seen such a depressing place. It smelt musty; and I saw a mouse pop out of a box and scuttle under a stillion.

'You'll have to put the cat down here,' I remarked.

'Ain't got one,' he replied sadly. 'Missis says it might suffocate the baby.'

'Oh.' Glancing up at the cobwebbed ceiling joints, I noticed beer trickling down the sides of two utilizers. 'Those utes look full to me.'

'Oh, are they!' he muttered. 'Lift 'em down for me, will you? I can't reach without the steps.'

I took them down and helped him to empty them into four buckets. The amount shocked me. I had never seen so much waste.

'What are you going to do with all this?' I asked.

'Bung it into that barrel o' mild there,' he replied casually.

Being by now almost an expert at judging contents, I kicked the barrel, and a hollow sound rang out. There were about sixteen gallons in it, I reckoned, and about eight gallons of waste in the buckets.

'But this is half empty,' I exclaimed, giving the barrel another kick.

'Well, what about it?' he growled.

'Won't it come out like soup?' I asked.

'No, it won't,' he snorted. 'That's all good beer in them buckets. It's only them ruddy barmaids; they will slop it all over the place. All amachures up there, they are. Can't get regular staff here; all the men work in the docks, and the girls in the factories. I daren't waste a drop of anything.'

I glanced at the horizontal beer pipes overhead. They were all coated inside with a film of greyish-yellow sediment.

'Who cleans the pipes?' I asked.

'Perce the potman,' he replied, flushing slightly. 'Every Saturday,' he added, evidently scenting the criticism in my question.

'Saturday!' I exclaimed. 'What makes the fool choose the busiest day of the week?'

'He don't choose it,' replied Mr. Grainger with a superior smile. 'I tell him. It's the proper day. Any publican will tell you that. Saturday is always pipes day.'

It was not at the Gorget Hotel, but I let that pass.

'You got to have method in this line,' he added.

I gaped. I had only known him a few minutes, but I could not imagine anyone ever crediting him with method. The pipes looked as if they had not been touched for weeks.

'Oh, quite!' I said.

'You'll soon learn,' he smiled. 'Don't be afraid to ask me anything.'

'Thanks very much,' I murmured, wondering modestly which of the two of us knew the least about cellar work.

I helped to carry the buckets across the cellar, and then watched my new instructor in the art of beer-keeping empty them into the barrel and effectually ruin what had once been sixteen gallons or so of good mild ale. By that time he had forgotten why he came down into the cellar.

'Might as well go up now,' he muttered. 'Like to serve in the public?'

'All right,' I said despondently.

He waddled up the steps ahead of me, switched off the cellar lights at the top, and closed the door.

'No need to tell you the prices,' he said, nodding sadly at the rows of dusty bottles under the public-bar counter. 'They're all chalked on the shelves, see? Everything is marked because of the staff. They're all tempo'ry. Draught beer is marked on the splash-board; spirits on a bit o' paper by the till. Okay?'

I noticed that the bottles had been put on the shelves straight from the boxes without being polished; that the shelves were dirty; that the pewter was tarnished a dull dark-grey colour. There were puddles of beer on the counter; glasses were cloudy and smeared with fingermarks. The electric-light bulbs were spattered with fly spots. I wondered what I would learn in such a house except how things should not be done. I felt thoroughly miserable.

'Fine, thanks,' I said dejectedly.

'Righto, ask me if you want to know anything,' he said, and went into the saloon.

I glanced at my colleagues. A barman and a barmaid were on duty. The man was sipping a glass of gin; the woman had a half-finished glass of Guinness under the counter; and they were both smoking. Hmm! They were making themselves at home all right. I felt I needed something myself. I went to the till and glanced at the spirit prices. After all, why not? When in Rome do as the Romans do. Reaching for the whisky, I poured myself a double, paid for it, and drank it; and my new colleagues smiled appreciatively.

The barman came to speak to me.

'You the chap wot's coming to learn the trade?'

'Yes,' I smiled.

He grinned.

'You don't have to pay for your drinks, chum.'

'Oh, I dunno,' I said. 'Fair's fair. Someone's got to pay for 'em.'

'You can always make 'em up, you know.'

'Eh! How d'you mean?'

'Well, use your head.'

'Sorry,' I said, bristling slightly, because I didn't like being told to use my head—especially by a fellow who'd just asked me if I was the chap 'wot's' coming to learn the trade. Snobbish, I suppose, but there you are. 'I don't quite get you,' I muttered.

'Well, there's no need to overflow the measure, is there?' he smirked. 'A couple or three doubles and you can easy make up a single for yourself, mate.'

'Oh, I see! Hmm—I think I'd rather pay.'

A huge stevedore had just come in, looking tired after a long day in the docks, and I went to serve him.

'Watch this big beggar,' the barman whispered, 'he's a swine. The governor's going to bar 'im when he can pluck up the courage.'

'Okay,' I muttered.

'Ghissile,' said the stevedore.

'I beg your pardon?'

'Ghissile,' he said again, and turned to speak to someone at the other side of the room.

I was completely mystified.

'Er—excuse me,' I said. 'What did you say?'

There was no answer.

'Excuse me,' I said once more. 'Hoy!'

There was still no reply, so I touched his arm. He whipped round.

'Keep yer blooming 'ands off me.'

'Sorry,' I said angrily. 'But what d'you want?'

'Blimey! 'Ow many more times! Don't you know what ile is?'

'Oh, you want a pint of ale, eh?'

'If I wanted a pint I'd ask for it. Ghissile, I says.'

'Half a pint?'

'Yus.' He flung a handful of coppers on the counter.

Still restraining my temper, I served him with half a pint of ale, and counted the money.

'New to the game, ain't yer?' he sneered.

'I know the price of mild ale,' I answered. 'This is a penny short.'

'No, it ain't.'

I counted the coins one by one in front of him.

'Sorry, but I'm afraid it is.'

'Wasn't short when I put it dahn.'

'Come on,' I said irritably, 'give me another penny, man; people are waiting to be served.'

A brawny hand reached for the ale, and I snatched it away.

'No, you don't!'

'All right,' he growled, and threw a penny rudely on the counter.

It bounced up and cut my lip.

'You swine!'

There was a curt laugh, and then I lost my temper. Grabbing the penny from the floor, I swept the other coins into my hand, and hurled them into his face.

With an oath, he drew back his right fist and flung a full-arm swing across the counter. It didn't hit me because I had only to step out of reach; but it told me something. The fellow couldn't box—not that I'm much of a boxer myself, because a chap my size can so seldom find anyone to spar with—but he was my weight, a good ten years younger, and obviously stronger. There was no doubt about his strength. The marks of his strenuous calling were manifest in the bulging muscles rippling under the thin thread of his dungarees, and in his massive calloused hands. A formidable opponent, I thought. Better call a policeman. But what the heck! My lip was bleeding, and smarting; and the brute was preparing for another long-arm swipe. Automatically, my left arm jerked forward, and my fist shot up. It wasn't much of a blow, and there was very little weight behind it, owing to the intervening counter; but he happened to be swaying towards me with his next blow, and it clicked home on that painful spot where the gristle at the bottom of the nose meets the top of the upper lip. It would have been bad enough for him if I had been wearing gloves, but with my bare fist it must have been agony. Blood spurted from his nostrils, and tears welled in his eyes. That was my chance. I slithered across the counter to finish the job.

Some people who were on their way out had stopped to watch, and one of them was providentially holding the door open. Grinning to myself, I grabbed the stevedore by the collar of his dungaree jacket, and throwing myself backwards, gave a mighty heave. It was an old throw, practised probably since men first wore clothes; and taken unawares, the huge fellow staggered backwards across the room on his heels and crashed on to the fibre mat outside. I followed, and the door swung shut behind the two of us.

Now, this was not sport; so the Queensberry Rules did *not* come into it. It was business. In the language of the police courts, this beast had behaved in a manner whereby a breach of the peace was occasioned. He had made trouble, and for no reason at all, and without even the excuse of drunkenness; and he had to be punished. Also, for the sake of safety; for there were women in the house, and he had been throwing things; he had to be put out of action. I did both, simply and efficiently, with a well-shod foot applied commandowise where it hurt. Then walking round the corner to the next street, I re-entered the house by the private bar entrance; and sporting customers who had rushed out to see the fun found him alone and inert on his back, breathing stertorously into the evening air. One of them, who had no love for the police, kindly helped Perce the potman to lug him clear of the doormat, so that he no longer lay on licensed premises.

With slightly shaking fingers I lit a cigarette, and buying myself a whisky-and-soda to calm my nerves, went quietly back to work.

'Pint,' grinned an old man shuffling to the counter.

'Ale?' I inquired.

'Yus,' said he. ' 'Andled 'im nice, you did, mate. 'Bout time 'e 'ad what was coming to 'im. Been barred from most o' the pubs round 'ere, 'e 'as.'

'Oh, has he!'

'Yus; but the governor 'ere, he's afraid of 'im.'

'Ghissarf,' said another customer.

'What's the hell's that?' I laughed.

The barman translated.

'Half o' bitter.'

'Oh . . .? How d'you know he doesn't want ale?'

'He'd have said "ghissile" if he wanted 'arf o' ale,' smiled the barman. ' "Ghissarf" means 'arf o' bitter.'

'I see. And suppose he wanted a pint of bitter?'

'Then he'd say "Pinta bi'er", o' course. If he wanted a pint of ale he'd say "Pint". "Ghissile" is 'arf of ale, and "ghissarf" is 'arf o' bitter.'

'Well, well!' said I. 'To think I was born in this town! And here I am learning cockney.'

'It ain't cockney!' snorted the barman. 'They speak that up Bow way.'

'What is it then?'

'Just the way they talk round here, that's all. There's plenty o' different ways of talking in London, you know.'

'Yes, I suppose there are. It's getting a big place now. You must teach me some more.'

But there was no time to study the local vernacular just then. Mr. Grainger had heard about the fracas with the stevedore; and he came in ranting, and wringing his hands.

'You didn't ought to have done that, Mr. Day. You didn't ought to have done it. What'll I do if he comes back?'

'Don't worry,' I grinned. 'Bullies never come back once they're licked.'

'Oh, don't they!' he moaned. 'You wait till you've been in this district as long as I have. He'll come in on Saturday with all his mates.'

'Rot!' said I. 'His mates will feel safer without him when they hear how he was treated.'

'You wait. You wait. Anyway, don't do it again. You're not to do it again.'

'All right; but suppose he does come back; and he starts throwing things at me? What do I do then?'

'Call me.'

'And what will you do?' I asked, trying not to smile.

'Phone for the police.'

'I see; and what do I do while we're waiting for the police? Let him go on throwing things at me?'

'Never mind that; you're not to do it again.'

'But I do mind,' I laughed. 'I mind very much.'

'You must try and keep your temper.'

'All right. I'll try until he starts throwing things at me.'

'Ghissile 'n staht,' said a customer testily.

'Righto, mate; coming up,' I said. 'Er—let me see, what's that? Half of ale with a bottle of stout?'

'Yus.'

Irene wandered in from the saloon.

'Hallo, cocky, how are you getting on?'

'Fine, thanks. I'd forgotten all about you. How long have you been down?'

'Ages. I hear you've thrown half the population of Poplar into the street.'

'Only one of 'em. The swine cut my lip open.'

'Oh, darling! do be careful.'

'I was—jolly careful. I say, sweetheart, it's a bit rough here. If you have any trouble in the saloon don't bother with that bladder of lard Grainger, yell for me at the top of your voice. Get me?'

'Righto, dear.'

'I don't think we ought to stay here; it's no place for you.'

'Oh, I'm all right; I'm enjoying myself. They call me Ireen in the saloon.'

'No! Do they really!'

'Mm. What do they call you?'

'Well, I won't soil your ears by repeating what that stevedore called me.'

' 'Ere!' cried a voice. 'Wot's this 'ere?'

'Just a sec,' I said.

A burly navvy was holding a mug of ale up to the light.

'Wot's this 'ere?' he asked again, gruffly.

A glance was enough to show me what was wrong. It was some of the ale Mr. Grainger had just spoilt. Taking the mug, I emptied it into a drip can, and just to make sure, refilled it and held it to the light.

'Hmm—it is cloudy, isn't it!' I muttered. I drew off two or three pints and tried again. It was worse.

A steadily increasing chorus of 'Wot's this 'ere?'

By that time mugs were being raised in all parts of the room, to a steadily increasing chorus of 'Wot's this 'ere?'

I hurried to the saloon.

'Mr. Grainger, that mild ale is coming up muddy.'

'Can't help it; they got to drink it.'

'But they won't.'

'They'll have to. I can't throw all that good beer away. Look what I'm up against. Look at that Rosie there!'

I looked; and the sight shocked me.

Irene and I had learnt to fill a mug to the brim without spilling a drop; but Rosie was pumping up beer as if she were trying to put a fire out, and the sump and all the drip cans were swilling with it.

'Yes, I can see she enjoys wasting the stuff,' I said; 'but what about all those fellows in the public bar? It's like an eclipse of the sun in there, with them all peering out of the windows through their mugs.'

'Can't help that.'

'Well, can't you come and do something? There'll be a riot in a minute.'

'What's the matter with you doing something? You're serving there.'

That annoyed me. I'd been proud of my cellar work at the Gorget Hotel; and it was only bad cellar work that had caused the situation.

'Look here, old boy,' I said, 'I don't mind dealing with a rowdy customer now and again when necessary, but this is a managerial job; and what's more, you are doing the cellar work.'

The double thrust went home. He blushed.

'All right,' he mumbled, 'use the end pump.'

'Which end?'

'The far end.'

I tried that one and found the ale was good. When all the cloudy stuff had been exchanged, the sump was two inches deep with it and every drip can brimming. I glanced at the barman.

'What the heck are we going to do with all this?' I asked him. 'It ought to be running down into the ute.' Then I remembered the utilizers had just been emptied. 'Oh, I suppose the taps are still turned off. I'd better tell the governor.'

The barman laughed.

'You won't get 'im into the cellar before closing time.'

'Why?' I asked.

' 'Cos he'd 'ave to come through this bar to get there, o' course; and he's frightened o' that stevedore coming back.'

'Tch! I'll go and do it myself.'

I slithered down the steps, and while in the cellar, slipped the dipstick into the spoilt ale. A rough calculation at the public-bar price showed there was about twelve pounds' worth left. Twelve pounds' worth of good ale ruined by sheer inefficiency. I climbed slowly up to the ground floor, thinking deeply, and then beckoned Irene from the saloon.

'Look here, sweetheart, get hold of that Rosie idiot and see if you can teach her how to pull up a mug of beer, will you? There's twelve quids' worth of mild ale in the cellar that looks like curdled gravy. That's over a week's wages, and a chap can't chuck that away every day. This fool Grainger must be helped in spite of himself; besides, he may be the kind of ass who'll put the blame on us if the directors find out about it. He's just that cowardly type.'

'All right, darling, I'll have a go at her. She may listen to me, because she's just asked me where I get my lipstick; not that it'll be much use to her, with her colouring, but still.'

I turned to the barman.

'I vote we try and make a little less waste in here, old boy, shall we?'

'Mm-hm,' he grunted unenthusiastically.

'I mean, it all has to go back into the barrel; and then it makes the stuff cloudy, and the customers grumble, and it's so damned unpleasant for us. Isn't it?'

'S'pose so.'

'That's the style!' I cried encouragingly. 'And will you ask the girl to do the same?' I added, with a nod at the barmaid.

'That's my wife,' he snapped.

'Oh!' It hadn't occurred to me that such a scruffy-looking bit would have a husband. 'Well then, you can *tell* her,' I grinned maliciously. 'That's fine!' I beckoned Irene from the saloon again. 'Listen, sweety pie, if you want me I shall be in the cellar. I'm going to give it a good cleaning. It's like a pig-sty down there.'

'All right; but don't overdo it; it's not our cellar.'

'I know; but I don't like serving cloudy beer. If you have any trouble stamp on the floor, and I'll come dashing up with a mallet.'

'Righto, cocky.'

Before starting, I walked round the cellar and made a plan of action. Then I found the hot water was only luke-warm; but still, that was better than cold; so I located the soda, washed and scrubbed the two utilizers and all the buckets, and then found some rags and metal polish, and cleaned the funnels and the dipstick. After that I swept a couple of barrow-loads of dust and rubbish to the foot of the steps, and scrubbed and mopped the floor. The pipes I had to leave, because they needed hot water; but I put out the wire and brushes, and the spanners, ready for use the next day, and then polished all the beer taps that were in use and started on the spare ones.

While doing all those jobs I also kept an eye on the casks of mild ale that were in use, testing them with the dipstick every quarter of an hour, and easing into them a little at a time as much as I dared of the twelve pounds' worth of cloudy ale. It went much against the grain, but I felt that the idiot Grainger had to be helped for our own sakes; in other words, that if I could get the waste under control, and keep it there, it might be a point in our favour with the directors of the firm.

I was still polishing the spare beer taps when Mr. Grainger came waddling down the stone steps.

'Hallo!' he said. 'Been having a clean-up?'

'Yes,' I replied, smiling naively in anticipation of some appreciation of my efforts. 'Thought I might as well.'

He glanced at the tap in my hand.

'You don't want to worry about them taps,' he growled. 'I don't believe in eyewash; it don't affect the beer.'

I didn't say anything; and he wandered round the cellar and came to the brushes and spanners laid out ready for cleaning the pipes in the morning.

'You don't want to touch them pipes either,' he muttered. 'That's Perce's work.'

'He doesn't make much of a job of them,' I remarked.

Mr. Grainger flushed.

'He might do better,' he admitted. 'I'll have to tell him about 'em. But you don't want to interfere with his work; he might turn nasty.'

'That would be a pity,' I muttered, beginning to lose my temper.

'You can't afford to upset your staff these days,' he observed. 'I'll put these things back. Where did you find them?'

'All over the blasted cellar,' I snorted.

'Oh!' He looked taken aback. 'Well, I'll put them in the corner here. If Perce thinks they've been interfered with he might leave.'

'That *would* be a loss, wouldn't it!' I said sarcastically.

To my amazement that was taken seriously.

'Yes,' he agreed. 'You can't get staff nowadays. Why don't you leave them taps? You're only wasting metal polish and putting up the expenses. If you want something to do you can give this floor a mop over. It don't do to leave a cellar floor too wet.'

'All right, I'll mop it again if you like,' I growled, fuming inwardly.

'The brewers don't like to see a cellar floor all wet,' he added.

'Don't they?' I muttered.

'No.'

'Why?' I asked through clenched teeth.

'Because it don't look nice. You want to remember that when you get your own house.'

'I will,' I said, stifling a snort. 'Thanks for telling me.'

'That's all right,' he smiled, apparently pleased at this unexpected tribute to his superior knowledge. 'Always ask me if you want to know anything.'

I stared at him in astonishment. Was he mad? He lit a cigarette and dropped the matchstick on the floor.

'I've just scrubbed this ruddy floor,' I growled.

'Yes, I see you have,' he smiled; 'but you've left it too wet.' He waddled importantly across the cellar and up the steps, obviously pleased with the way he had shown his authority, and at the same time encouraged a beginner to give of his best.

I sat on a box of brown ales and lit a cigarette, and swore quietly to myself for several incandescent seconds.

'Well, of all the jumped-up . . . !'

Presently I heard him calling Time in the saloon, and went up, and through the doorway from the public bar, saw him beaming benignly at his customers.

This, we were to learn, was always his big moment of the day, and the only part of it when he really liked any of his customers.

'Time, *gentlemen*, PLEASE!' he screeched joyfully every few seconds; and occasionally he whistled a few bars of some airy tune. He loved closing time.

I glared at the back of his head, and threw away my cigarette end. I was in a bad temper, although at the same time pleased with myself; because I knew I had done a good evening's work even if it had been unappreciated. Also, I was very tired, and disappointed at being sent to such a badly managed house. In that complicated frame of mind it seemed to me something soothing, in the way of a pick-me-up, was needed, especially as I had forgotten to have

Fatty Grainger loved shouting 'Time'

my supper, and in consequence felt a little weak. In fact, it
appeared to be the occasion for something pretty bracing. I
rather fancied a dog's nose—but not made with Mr.
Grainger's bitter! So instead, I mixed a bottle of light ale
with the gin, and swallowed it in two long appreciative
draughts.

'Ghissile,' said someone.

I glared and said it was too late, and swinging myself over
the counter, propped the street door open with a chair,
and went from table to table collecting glasses, pausing
every now and then to say good-night and mention the
time.

It was some moments before the dog's nose took effect, so
my bad temper was probably still apparent in my expression; and customers who had witnessed the stevedore
incident drank up quickly and went out; others, assuming
it was later than they thought, meekly followed, with the
result that all the public-bar customers—to their disgust and
considerable surprise—found themselves in the street with
the doors locked behind them within a few minutes of the
official closing time; and Irene and I heard afterwards that
the news ran round the district like wildfire.

'Watch yerself at the Anchor, mate,' became the local
slogan. 'There's a big b . . .'

Meanwhile, the temporary barman and his wife had gone
home and left me to clear up and wash the glasses. As I
turned on the hot tap and tested the now stone-cold water,
Mr. Grainger looked in from the saloon.

'Get 'em out as quick as you can, Mr. Day,' he said.

'There's no one in here,' I grinned.

'Oh . . .?' He peered into the room unbelievingly. 'I
didn't 'ear you shouting.'

'I didn't,' I said. 'I just told them the time and said good-night.'

That was too much for Mr. Grainger. He believed in method.

'That's no good,' he snorted. 'You want to let 'em hear you. That's the proper way to get 'em out. Like this.' He turned and bellowed into the saloon. 'Time, ladies and *gents*, PLEASE!'

No one took the slightest notice, not even Irene and I who were supposed to be being taught how to run a public house.

IX

As Mr. Grainger's permanently temporary staff (if it may be
so termed) refused to stay and clear up after closing time,
and Perce the potman reckoned it was not his expletive job,
that duty had always fallen to Mr. Grainger himself, before
Irene and I came. His wife did sometimes give him a little
help in the evening if she were not too tired after caring for
Prebern all day, but as her help consisted almost entirely in
telling him what to do next it was not really of any great
value, except perhaps as moral support. Even then the
moral was doubtful, for she considered her most important
duty was to collect the lees from all the used lemonade
bottles in a pint mug, and after fortifying some of them
with gin, and in turn fortifying herself, to re-bottle the
remainder for sale the next day. She seemed to imagine that
in some magical way this trifling economy offset the cost of
the gin, although that was often quite a lot. In fact, she
sometimes had to open fresh bottles of lemonade; but by
then, of course, she was past caring.

Meanwhile Mr. Grainger rinsed—we won't say washed—
the glasses, wiped the counters and checked the takings.
After that he had to make the takings agree with the till
readings, which sometimes took him up to two or even three
hours, because he was not a very brilliant accountant, and
—and this is important—he had to check the change rack at
the same time.

The change rack—which was so important—was used in
conjunction with both tills, and consisted of a number of
tiny shelves fastened to a board on which there were rows of

clips for holding notes. Little heaps of money to the value of either ten or twenty shillings each were put on the shelves, the idea being that notes could be clipped to the board and exchanged for smaller currency without the trouble of counting, thus saving time; and also—according to the clever salesman who landed the firm with it—the rack was supposed to show the publican *where he was at any time of the day*; though how, no one ever discovered, except perhaps Mr. Marnes who bought the thing, and maybe the clever salesman. Nearly every public house has one, though it seldom seems to be used other than as a happy resting-place for lost pipes, broken lighters, stray trouser buttons, and so forth. Mr. Lawson at the Gorget Hotel never touched his, except on inspection days when he dressed it with a little silver and a few notes to please Mr. Marnes; nor did the manager of a house to which we were sent later on; both of them saying they had no time to fiddle about folding notes and counting silly little heaps of silver. They were far too busy seeing that their staff didn't fiddle the till; and as for knowing where they were, they didn't care a bee. But Mr. Grainger was a man of method, it will be remembered; he used his. That it failed lamentably to show him where he was at any time whatsoever, concerned him not in the slightest degree, because he had never known where he was in all his life, so he was quite used to that. All he was concerned with was the method; and he didn't care whether it was a good method or a bad one—he believed in it. If it was good, okay; if it wasn't, then it was up to the firm. The firm had sent him the rack, and he was jolly well going to use it. Secretly, he loved the thing, because it gave him such opportunities for rushing about and looking important. During busy sessions he was so occupied dashing from bar to bar with fistfuls of silver and folded ten-shilling notes, and losing pound ones, and bumping into barmaids, and then knocking little piles of silver under the counter, and searching for coins at the back of the bottled beer, that he had little time for anything else.

To complicate matters, his friends and relations, who came in nearly every day, ostensibly to help, but actually for free drinks and easy money, misused the thing in every conceivable way, so that hardly a day passed without one till being several pounds down and the other several pounds up. Sometimes the amounts tallied very roughly, but mostly they did not. Occasionally, to add to the gaiety of life, or merely because he made himself such a nuisance with the change rack, his relations would conspire together and hide some of the notes. Then when he came to cash-up he would spend hours fussing from till to till, and running up-and-downstairs between the safe and the saloon, and poring with ruffled hair over sheets of pencilled figures, all the while sustaining himself, first with Guinness and then with gin, until he was so drunk he had to go to bed; although by inclination he was an abstemious man. Then the next evening his relations would pretend to find the notes in some absurd place; and he would stand drinks all round, and spend the rest of the day wondering how he came to put them there. It never occurred to him that he was having his leg pulled.

Also, he settled bills with money taken from the rack, and from the tills, and then either mislaid the receipts, or forgot to make notes of the payments, or both. So, as can be imagined, cashing-up at the end of the day at the Block and Anchor was quite an operation. What is hard to imagine is how Irene and I ever managed to learn anything there; but we did, and more than the firm expected us to learn. But I am running ahead.

When at last we went upstairs at the end of our first evening we found a cottage pie waiting for us in the oven; and a very nice one it was too, because Mrs. Grainger was a very good cook. It was one of those cottage pies with everything but the kitchen stove in it: plenty of onions and bacon fat, and a good sprinkling of herbs, and bits of beef and mutton, and not too dry, and butter in the potato part. It was good. To follow, there was a very pleasant trifle with a dash of P. H. Kent and Company's sherry in it.

'Just the thing!' I cried appreciatively. 'I wanted something easy to eat.'

'Had a trying time?' Irene asked.

I told her about the cellar and how Mr. Grainger had reacted to my cleaning.

'I'm getting up at six tomorrow to do the pipes,' I added.

'Oh, darling, must you!' she cried. 'After that! It's not our pub, you know.'

'I know it isn't,' I sighed; 'and it's not our fault; but I just can't work in a pig-sty—and we can't keep on asking for moves. I vote we try and get the place shipshape between us; then, even if Fatty Grainger can't teach us anything, at least we may have time to teach ourselves something; besides——'

'Yes . . . ?'

'I want to show the ruddy directors I'm not soft.'

'All right,' smiled Irene. She always reacts to a challenge. 'I'm game. I'll get up with you and try and clean some of the grime from the cabinets, and do something about the glasses. You can hardly see through some of the glasses.'

'Terrible, aren't they!' I commented. 'Anyway, even if it

is a dirty house, the grub's not bad; and there's no luncheon trade. That's a weight off your mind.'

'Now-now!' she laughed. 'You're stepping on dangerous ground. Had enough to eat?'

'Yes, thanks, let's go to bed. I'm sleeping with you tonight.'

'Don't build on it,' she smirked; 'I'm tired.'

'Gertcha!' I grinned.

X

WE slept well, in spite of the double bed, and soon after six the next morning were down in the kitchen nosing into cupboards for tea. While Irene made it I put a couple of buckets of water on the gas-stove to give me a start with the beer pipes, and lit the boiler. Then feeling uncomfortable creeping about in someone else's kitchen, and having an unaccountable tendency to talk in whispers, we took everything downstairs; but it wasn't much better there. Drinking tea in the deserted saloon of an East End public house at half past six in the morning we found a somewhat eerie experience. It was rather like having a meal on the stage of an empty theatre amid the *décor* and scattered properties of Act III, Scene 2. The atmosphere was all wrong, and our voices rang flat. Quite apart from that, the smell of spilt beer and stale smoke from shag tobacco didn't go too well with the tea; so we gulped it down and went quickly to work.

I pumped the pipes full of hot soda-water first and left them to soak, and then went up and helped Irene with the high tiers of shelves behind the bars, which for some unknown reason publicans always call cabinets. Between us we collected from them nearly a bucketful of old pipes, odd gloves, counterfeit half-crowns, tobacco pouches, broken lighters, and so forth; and an amazing miscellany of valueless foreign coins.

'What a collection!' exclaimed Irene. 'Wonder when these shelves were done last. The year dot, I should think

I'd scrub them if we had any hot water. Think they'll take polish as they are?'

'Don't think so,' I said. 'Give them a good rub along the edges.'

We did that, and it made quite a difference; and by that time the water was running hot so I cleaned and rinsed the pipes. Then I helped Irene to re-wash, dry and polish all the glasses that she and I—and I mean she and I—had not washed the night before. We were still busy with these when Kate arrived with her paraphernalia for scrubbing the floors.

The saloon may have been an odd place for the enjoyment of morning tea, but Kate, with her mop and pail, fitted right into the picture. Ancient, scraggy, and even at that hour, incredibly dirty, she sported long-pointed court shoes with heels worn almost to the uppers, skirts down to the ground, and one of those funny little hats that were in vogue when Queen Victoria came to the throne, perched precariously on a knob of wispy grey hair.

'Good morning,' she said affably.

'Good morning,' said Irene and I.

She smiled coyly at me.

'I see you lit the boiler,' she simpered.

'Yes,' I smiled.

'Does you always get up early?' she inquired naively.

'No,' I frowned. 'You'll have to light it yourself to-morrow.'

'Oh!' She stopped smiling, and got down on her knees.

Although she was so fragile-looking she scrubbed the whole of the three floors herself, which was quite a feat considering her age. It is not suggested that she scrubbed them clean, but that is beside the point. She did scrub them.

She was still on her knees when at half past nine Mr. Grainger came into the saloon to prepare the house for opening.

'Good morning, Kate,' said he.

'Good morning, guv.'

Then he noticed Irene and me.

'Oh, hallo!' he exclaimed. 'Good morning!'

He seemed surprised to see us. After all, he was not used to willing workers. He noted the counters loaded with shining glasses, the properly dusted cabinets adorned with glistening bottles, and a general air of tidiness to which he was entirely unaccustomed; and his eyes lit with pleasure. But no praise flowed from his lips. He seemed rather to be thinking how excellently his few well-chosen words in the cellar the previous evening were bearing their merited fruit.

'Getting on all right?' he inquired condescendingly.

'Yes, thank you,' smiled Irene.

'Uh-huh,' I glowered, not liking his lordly tone.

'That's right,' he nodded, smiling importantly. 'Ask me anything you want to know. Better get your breakfast as soon as you've put them glasses away,' he added patronizingly. 'I'll go down and turn the beer on.'

'It's on,' I snapped.

'Oh, you've done it! That's fine!' He turned about and waddled happily out to the hall.

We could read his thoughts. If we wanted to do all the work it was okay by him; he was paid to manage, not to work. We heard him whistling cheerfully all the way up to the first floor, where (we imagined) he probably told his wife he had a couple of saps working for him.

Irene made an unladylike noise; and presently we went up and had our baths. After that we strolled into the kitchen to look for breakfast. We were very hungry then, after four hours' work, but all we could find was a smell of bacon hovering over some dirty crocks that had been used by the Graingers.

'What do we do now?' I asked.

'Find Lil,' replied Irene. 'Where do they live?'

'I only know their bedroom,' I said, following her out to the landing. 'That's it there.'

She knocked on the door; and presently Mrs. Grainger appeared, wearing an overcoat over her nightdress, and bedroom slippers.

'D'you want your breakfasts?'

'Yes, please.'

'Take what you like; there's plenty in the fridge. I'm just feeding Prebern. You'll be all right, won't you?' She smiled and shut the door.

'Well, I'm blowed!' exploded Irene. 'Have we to cook our own breakfast as well as clean the place!'

I laughed and went to the frigidaire.

It was nearly opening time when we finished our meal, so lighting cigarettes, we went down to the saloon, where we found Mr. Grainger setting out the tobacco, and cheese biscuits, and so forth.

'Where would you like us to serve?' I asked. 'Same as yesterday? Wife in here, and me in the public bar?'

'Yes, that'll be all right.'

'Who else is serving?' I inquired, after glancing into the other bars and seeing no one in either of them.

'Dunno,' he mumbled. 'I never know till they come. Don't suppose there'll be anyone—not for a bit anyway.'

'H'm,' I said thoughtfully. 'Good job we two are here. What would you do if we weren't?'

'Then the missis would *have* to come down,' he growled vindictively; 'but Rosie may be along presently. She said she might.'

At eleven o'clock he opened the doors, and some customers who had been waiting for that happy moment came crowding in.

Within a few minutes Irene and I were serving as hard as we could, each of us doing the work of three people, while Mr. Grainger fussed backwards and forwards from bar to bar with handfuls of silver and notes, making up the change rack. I kept elbowing him out of the way, and Irene kept saying 'Excuse me, Mr. Grainger!' in a sort of musical-comedy voice; but he was determined to get the thing functioning. He seemed to think his success in life depended on it. Then suddenly, without a word of explanation, he disappeared, and we were left to work in comfort; though still very much rushed. Then the saloon ran out of gin, and Irene came running into the public bar.

'Got any gin, cock?'

'Only a quarter of a bottle. Where's Fatty?'

'Vanished. Haven't seen him for ages.'

'Use this, then; I'll go and find him.' I gave her my quarter of a bottle, and running through the saloon to the private door, shouted up the stairs: '*Mr. Grainger! Mr. Grainger!*'

His wife came on to the landing.

'He's gone to the bank.'

'We've run out of gin,' I yelled. 'Can you get us some?'

'No. He's got the keys.'

'Oh!' I ran back to my bar, where thirsty customers were already clamouring for service, and pulled up a few beers.

D

Then the bitter pump ran dry. 'Cripes !' I dashed through to
the stairs again. 'MRS. GRAINGER ! MRS. GRAINGER !'

'Yes ?'

'Is the governor back ?'

'No.'

'Heck !' I ran into the saloon, scrambled under the flap,
and grabbed Irene by an elbow. 'How's your bitter, girl ?'

'Just run out.'

'Oh, my gosh !' I dashed into my own bar, and slithered
down the steps into the cellar, and found that the fool
Grainger had forgotten to tap the next two barrels. I knew,
of course, that it was wrong to tap bitter immediately before
use, but what could I do ! Well, it was the governor's fault if
it came up cloudy. I grabbed a mallet, tapped the two
barrels as carefully as I could so as to disturb the sediment
as little as possible, connected the pipes and dashed upstairs
again.

'Ghissile.'

'Two mild-and-bitters.'

'Four stahts 'n a pint.'

'Come on, mate, 'urry up.'

'All right, blast you ! I've only got two hands.'

'*Bill !*'

I looked round and saw Irene in the doorway.

'Yes ?'

'I've run out of rum.'

'*Bai-lah, bilang minum beer*' (Okay, tell 'em to drink beer),
I grinned, speaking in Malay so that the customers wouldn't
understand me. 'All right, mate, coming up. Four and seven,
please. Can't you give me the right amount ?'

'*Bill !*' It was Irene again. 'My mild's off now.'

'*Chi ! pora, pen-nai*' (Heck ! run away, bitch), I fumed,

in Tamil this time. '*Yenukku mele remba kashtum iruki parkilia?*'

'Yes, darling,' replied Irene meekly. 'I can see you're in trouble; but what shall I do? It's worse in here.'

'Serve from this pump for a bit.'

'*Bai-lah*; but I shall only get behindhand.'

'Can't help that. I wish that *sinna sathi pandiandi*' (low-caste son of a pig) 'Grainger would come back.'

Unknown to either of us, he had come back; and when Irene took some mugs of ale to her customers in the saloon she found him checking the change rack.

'Oh, there you are, Mr. Grainger! We've run out of gin and rum, and my ale's off.'

'Tell Mr. Day to put another barrel on. I'll get some gin and rum in a minute.'

Irene came to see me.

'Fatty's back, and he wants you to put another ale on for the saloon.'

'Why can't he do it?'

'He's still doing the change rack.'

I raged into the saloon.

'I say, for heaven's sake, man, leave that perishing machine alone. There's no gin and rum, and the ale's off in here, and the customers are three deep in every bar, waiting to be served.'

He flared up.

'Here! Who d'you think you're talking to?'

'Oh, come on, man, we want some gin and rum.'

'Well, I'll get it when I've done this rack.'

'But customers are waiting.'

'Oh, all right. Go and put an ale on.'

I ran down into the cellar, connected a fresh barrel, and

rushed upstairs again. Some minutes later I heard Rosie's
voice in the saloon, and looked in to ask her to run along
and tell Mr. Grainger to hurry up with the gin and rum ; but
he had already brought it. He had stopped to fiddle with
the change rack again. I glared at him.

'Come on, man, stop playing with that ruddy thing.
They're three deep in my bar.'

He flushed, and snatching up the bottles, followed me
into the public bar, muttering under his breath. It was a
good twenty minutes before order was restored : long
enough for me to decide that it was high time the Block and
Anchor had a proper cellarman. When he had simmered
down I put it tactfully to him.

'How would you like me to take over the cellar while
you're short of staff, Mr. Grainger ? It might help you.
Eh ?'

'What d'you know about cellar work ? You ain't been in
the line five minutes.'

'I did it at the Gorget.'

'Oh ! Oh, did you !' He thought the proposition over,
pondering it deeply.

He made me smile. His moonlike face was a poker-
player's dream, with every thought scampering over it for
all the world to see. It reflected every card in his hand. He
was obviously not keen on having a learner nosing about in
his cellar. On the other hand, I was there to learn—and
seemed to like work. Strange ! All the same, the directors
might think it funny if they heard he had refused the
offer.

'Oh, all right,' he said ungraciously. 'If you done it at the
Gorget I suppose you can do it here ; but, mind you, you'll
have to keep it clean.'

'Sure!' I said, gritting my teeth. 'Like it was when I came, eh?'

He ignored that.

'And don't touch the pipes,' he added. 'That's Perce's job. I don't want him upset.'

'Okay,' I replied submissively; and refraining from any mention of the fact that I had cleaned the pipes that morning, I added quickly, before he could get it in, 'I'll ask you if I want to know anything.'

That so pleased him that he immediately forgave me for, what he probably considered, my previous insolence, assuming I suppose that I was nervous at the time and didn't realize what I was saying; because I imagine he thought it quite natural for a beginner to be in awe of him. There was no vice in Mr. Grainger. He was just simple.

'That's right, Mr. Day,' he said pompously. 'You won't go far wrong if you do that. Always pleased to teach you anything about the line. I'm going up for my dinner now.'

It was then a minute past one. At five minutes past, his cousin Rosie went up for her dinner; and a quarter of an hour later the public bar ran out of gin again. I rushed through to the hall.

'*Mr. Grainger! Mr. Grainger!*'

'Yeth?' he lisped through a mouthful of food, from the landing.

'We want some more gin.'

'All ri', I'll throw the keys down.'

'Can't you come and get it yourself? I'm busy.'

'Eh!'

'You heard.'

A few moments later a very red-in-the-face manager

*'Why the heck couldn't you bring three
or four bottles?'*

came puffing into the public bar with a bottle of gin in his
hand.

'You want to be a bit more respectful, Mr. Day ; I'm the
boss here.'

'Eh?' I said, pulling up beer as fast as I could. 'What's
that? Put the gin in the rack, will you? I'm a bit rushed.
Why the heck couldn't you bring three or four bottles?
That'll be gone in a few minutes; and I can't keep on
shouting up the stairs for you.'

'Come on, guv, two gins,' growled a customer. 'We've
been waiting long enough for 'em.'

The guv flushed and poured them out.

'I'm going to fill the utes again now,' I said, and ran down the steps into the cellar before he could answer.

I was gradually getting rid of the half-barrel of spoilt ale, partly by filling the utilizers with it, and partly by easing a few pints into the barrels that were in use whenever I had the chance. It was disappearing quite nicely. When I had filled the utilizers I sat on an upturned kilderkin to enjoy a cigarette; and as I smoked, the noises in the public bar came to me through the ceiling, the scraping of chairs, footsteps on the oilcloth, and the hum of voices; but what pleased me most was the sound of Fatty Grainger's shoes clomping up and down behind the counter. It will do him good to do some work, I thought, smiling to myself. Occasionally I heard voices raised in exasperation.

'Come on, guv, I'm next.'

'Why don't you get some barmaids to 'elp you?'

I visualized him fuming at the thought of his nice dinner congealing on its plate in the kitchen. He obviously loved his food; and the mental picture added quite a lot to the enjoyment of my cigarette. Presently I squeezed out the stub and went upstairs.

'Two pints an' a staht.'

'Okay; coming up.' When I went to the till I noticed that the new bottle of gin was nearly empty. 'Better get some more gin before you go up to finish your dinner,' I muttered vindictively.

He went straight to the spirit store and fetched four bottles without a word, and thumped them down beside the till. Then he went upstairs, and stayed there for the rest of the session; so I suppose he won that round. At half past two his stumpy figure materialized as if by magic in the middle of the saloon, almost hidden among some people of normal size.

'Time, ladies and *gents*, PLEASE!' he bellowed, beaming like a Cheshire cat.

Rosie snatched out her puff, and after shaking it nonchalantly over a customer's beer and smothering her face in powder, started for home.

'See you tonight, Ron,' she shouted to Mr. Grainger, to his annoyance, as she went out.

Perce the potman, dirty, middle-aged, and of sombre aspect, came suddenly to life, and seizing a broom, spent a thoughtful seven minutes pushing cigarette ends and matchsticks under the corner chairs, and disappeared with the last customer. Then Mr. Grainger bolted the doors, locked the tills, and went upstairs, leaving Irene and me to wash the glasses and tidy the bars.

At a quarter past three I wiped my hands on a glass-cloth and lit a cigarette.

'I feel quite tired,' I remarked.

'So do I,' said Irene. 'Well, we can't wonder; we've been on the go since six, and it was past one when we went to bed last night.'

'Looks as if Fatty and Lil have packed up work now we've come,' I muttered. 'Think he's turned the beer off? I'd better go and see.'

'Oh, leave it. You tire yourself out trying to do everything.'

'But suppose a pipe cracks and a whole barrel of beer runs away!'

'That's his lookout. He should look after his beer.'

'But I'm cellarman now. I'd better go and see.'

'All right. Would you like a drink?'

'I wouldn't mind a pink gin.'

'Nor would I. I'll pour them out. Hurry up.'

I ran down and turned off the beer.

'Here's your drink,' said Irene when I returned. 'Put the money in the till, darling, before you forget.'

'Can't; it's locked.'

'Oh. Well, put it on top, and we'll tell him this evening like we used to at the Gorget.'

'No, I'm damned if I will,' I cried. The tiredness had made me irritable. 'I'm not going to be barman and cellar-man, and clean the house, and cook my own meals, and keep the manager up to his work, all for two-pound-ten a week, even if I am supposed to be being taught a job; which, by the way, I jolly well ain't. Dash it! we're a pretty good investment for this firm; they can buy us a drink occasionally.'

Irene laughed.

'I don't know that you aren't right, except that——' She broke off in mid-sentence.

'Except what?' I asked.

'Well——'

'I know what you mean: we mustn't let the old morals deteriorate.' I grinned and put the money on the till. 'Now let's have another to celebrate.'

'Celebrate what?'

'Our amazing honesty.' I mixed two more. 'Fatty seems to trust us too; or has he just forgotten to put the spirits away?'

'Forgotten, I should think,' smiled Irene.

I added the money for the second two drinks to the pile on the till—and paused.

'I say, we shall have to watch these double gins, sweety pie. If we're going to have a couple o' doubles every time we feel tired it's going to make our five-pounds-a-week joint screw look pretty silly at the end of the month. Make our ten pounds look silly, as far as that goes. I think I'll try and cultivate a taste for bitter.'

'That's an idea; but why not mild ale? That's cheaper still.'

'No fear! All the muck goes into that.'

'Oh, I forgot. Well, bitter is not too expensive. I suppose all publicans have to come to some decision about their drinks.'

'Must do, I should think—it's so damned easy otherwise, isn't it?'

'Mm. I had a double before these, because I was so tired.'

'Did you, by Jove! Well, so did I, as a matter o' fact. That's six doubles between us. Dash it, that's more than our day's wages, and there's the evening session to come yet. I'm switching over to beer.'

'Righto, boy; and I'll concentrate on Guinness.'

'No need to concentrate, my beautiful.'

'Well, you know what I mean.'

'Sure. Let's go and feed.'

We went upstairs, and found Mrs. Grainger putting cheese and pickled onions on the kitchen table.

'I'm giving you this for now,' she said. 'I expect you're used to having your dinner in the evening, aren't you?'

'Well, we were before we came into this business,' said Irene, wondering how Mrs. Grainger had guessed.

'That's all right, then. There's no cook to worry about, thank goodness, as we don't do lunches.' Mrs. Grainger smiled, and jerked a thumb towards the frigidaire. 'You'll find the butter on the top shelf. We always keep that for ourselves, and use margarine for the snacks. Customers don't notice it in sandwiches.'

Irene and I grinned appreciatively.

'No sense in being in the catering trade if you don't look after yourselves,' chuckled Mrs. Grainger.

'None at all,' agreed Irene.

'Good-bye,' said Mrs. Grainger unexpectedly.

'Good-bye,' said Irene and I without thinking what we were saying.

Mrs. Grainger went out and closed the door.

'What on earth did she say good-bye for?' tittered Irene.

'Don't ask me,' I giggled. 'She's always saying things like that.'

'Shy, I suppose,' observed Irene, carving a hunk of cheese. 'Cut some bread, darling.'

A few minutes later the door opened, and Mrs. Grainger pushed a pram into the room.

'There you are!' she said, smiling at me. 'You can play with Prebern for a while.' Still smiling, she went out, and closed the door again.

Presently Irene and I thought we heard footsteps on the stairs. Then the front door slammed; and I went to the window.

'Well, I'm damned!' I muttered. 'They've both gone out!'

'What!' cried Irene. 'And left us alone with their brat!'

'Goo!' said Prebern.

'Dash it! this is the limit,' exclaimed Irene. 'I didn't bargain for this. A couple of baby-sitters! They must think we're soft.'

'Perhaps we are. Whatcher, Prebern!'

'Goo! Da da da da da.'

'Don't you call me Dada,' I grinned. 'I say, buddy, can't you see the likeness?'

'What? To Marnes? Don't be silly.'

'Dead spit, if you ask me. Goo goo, Prebern.'

'Da da da da.'

We finished our lunch and lit cigarettes.

'What are we going to do with this blasted infant?' asked Irene between puffs.

'Goo goo da da splut!' said Prebern matily.

'Want a smoke?' I inquired.

He frowned; but evidently he did want something.

I went to the pram and tickled his ribs; but he didn't seem to like it much. His frown deepened. He seemed to be concentrating on some grave matter. I tickled his ribs again. The frown grew deeper still.

'Er—I think I'll slip across the road,' I muttered suddenly. 'I want to buy a—er—er—er—a pencil.'

'A pencil!' Irene sprang from her chair. 'No you don't!' she cried, with a frightened look at Prebern. 'I don't know any more about babies than you do.'

'Eh!—what d'you mean?' I asked as innocently as I could.

'You know jolly well what I mean,' she scowled. 'You coward!'

'Oh—d'you think something has happened?'

'Turn him over if you're not sure.'

I investigated.

'Hm! I'm afraid it has.'

'And you were going to run away and leave me, you skunk!'

'Well, hang it, it's woman's work, isn't it! Anyway, what's the next move?'

'Scout round for diapers, or whatever the damn things are called—er—I suppose. By the way, is it—er . . . ?'

'No, I don't think so,' I muttered, after a good look. 'Only—er——'

'Thank heaven for that! I don't think I could have stood the other just after lunch. Keep him amused while I look in their bedroom.'

'There are some on that shelf by the cistern.'

'Oh, yes; and here's an apron. Come on, put him on my lap.'

Prebern thought all this great fun; and within a few minutes he was dry and safely pinned up again—a trifle amateurishly perhaps, but he seemed comfortable. I glanced at Irene.

'What about the pram?'

'Don't say that's wet as well!' she exclaimed. 'Is it?'

'Bit on the humid side,' I muttered. 'Hums a bit too.'

'Hell! We'd better put him in his cot. Here, take him; I'll probably have to make it.' She gave him to me and led the way into the bedroom. 'Hm! There doesn't seem to be one.'

'Perhaps there isn't. He was in the pram when I saw him yesterday. I'll leave him on the bed.'

'No, don't; he'll crawl off and break his neck.'

'Oh, lor! Then we'll have to take him up to our bed, and watch him.'

'Come on, then; we'll have a rest too. I'm tired enough.'

We took the newspapers upstairs, and lay on our bed with Prebern between us. Five minutes later we were all asleep.

At a quarter past five Prebern smacked me on the nose.

'Hallo, old boy! had a good sleep?' I glanced at my

watch. 'Heck!' It was late. I turned Prebern over just to make sure. 'Thank goodness. Hey! wake up, sweetheart; we open in a quarter of an hour.'

'Oh, bother! I've only just got to sleep.'

We took Prebern down to the kitchen, and were greeted by Mrs. Grainger.

'Oh, there you are!' she said. 'I've made you some tea; it's on the table. Has he been a good boy?'

'Might have been worse,' yawned Irene reaching for the milk jug.

We gulped a cup of tea each and went downstairs. At half past five Mr. Grainger unbolted the doors.

'Ghissile.'

'Ghissarf.'

'Two pints.'

XI

THAT evening Irene and I were again too busy to have our meal during the session; and when we went up for it, at ten minutes past midnight, we found it on the kitchen table uncooked. There was some liver, some peeled potatoes and a cabbage. So it was nearly two o'clock before we staggered to bed; but by half past six the next morning we were downstairs again, scrubbing cabinets and scouring pewter. We were determined to make a good show.

For breakfast that morning we found a pair of kippers put out for us. Irene picked them up and burst out laughing.

'What's the joke?' I asked.

'My hands,' she replied. 'Doesn't cleaning pewter make them in a mess. Look! They're jet black.'

'Same here,' I grinned. 'We look like a couple of charladies, don't we?'

On our way downstairs after breakfast we passed the real charlady, on her knees scrubbing the oilcloth.

'Hallo, Kate, scrubbing the stairs again!' cried Irene. 'What's the idea? You only did them yesterday.'

'Eh? What, dear?' inquired Kate, staring up uncomprehendingly, her rheumy eyes bursting with vacuity. 'Eh? What d'yer say, dear?'

'You don't scrub these stairs every day, do you?' Irene asked.

'O' course I does.'

'What! All of them! Right from the top of the house?'

'O' course.'

'But they're hardly used. The house is practically empty.'

That meant nothing to Kate. She didn't care if the stairs were never used, so long as she was paid to scrub them.

'We got to keep the place clean,' she mumbled.

'That's typical of this comic house,' I remarked, as we continued our way down to the saloon. 'The part where the money's made is filthy, and the part that's hardly used is scrubbed every day. Hallo! here's Fatty in the saloon. Good morning, Mr. Grainger.'

'Good morning, Mr. Day. Good morning, Mrs. Day. I see you've been having a go at the pewter. About time some-one did it.'

'Yes,' I agreed. 'That's what we thought. Why don't you let Kate spend more time down here?'

'What? On the pewter?'

'Yes.'

'Blimey! she wouldn't touch it.' Mr. Grainger laughed. 'She's a cleaner.'

'That's what I mean. Why not let her clean the pewter?'

'That's the barmaids' work.'

'But they never do it.'

'No, but they're supposed to.'

'In the meantime it's dirty.'

'Well, what can I do?'

'Get Kate on the job. She's only wasting her time now.'

'Wasting her time!' cried Mr. Grainger aghast.

'Yes. She's scrubbing stairs and landings. A soft broom would do all that in a few minutes.'

'Soft broom!' exclaimed Mr. Grainger. 'You can't scrub oilcloth with a soft broom. I like to keep my house clean. I've got a reputation to live up to.'

'But the oilcloth is clean,' I persisted. 'It was scrubbed yesterday, and it's hardly been walked on since; and there's plenty of cleaning to be done down here. Look at the pewter.'

'Yes, I am looking at it,' said Mr. Grainger grimly. 'It ain't half done. It ought to come up much better than this.'

I gave up, and went down into the cellar and turned the beer on; but when I came up again I had another go at the fool. It was nothing to do with me, in a way, but I felt that any improvement in the Block and Anchor while Irene and I were there might reflect to our credit.

'How does one get staff?' I asked him. 'I mean, if you want a new barmaid, for instance, how do you go about it?'

'Why? What's that got to do with you?'

'Well, I'm here to learn. You told me to ask you if I wanted to know anything.'

'Oh, I'll tell you all those sort o' things in good time. I can't teach you everything at once.'

'Ever try the Labour Exchange?'

'The Labour! Huh! They never send you anyone what's any good. I've given them up now.'

'Do you advertise?'

'Not me! You wait till you get your own house, and see what Head Office says to you if you waste money advertising.'

'But have you tried?'

'No, and I don't intend to. The barmaids wouldn't know anything about it if I did. They don't read newspapers; they only listen to the wireless.'

'What do you do?'

'Well, everybody knows I want staff. They got eyes, ain't they?'

'D'you mean the customers?'

'Of course. They can see I need staff. They're always telling me so.'

'Do they ever send you anyone?'

'When they knows of somebody.'

'I see.' I wondered idly how much the staff he obtained that way cost the firm in free drinks for friends.

I was still debating with myself whether to ask him or not, when he interrupted my thoughts with a sardonic laugh.

'You got a lot to learn in this line,' he sneered.

'Yes, I can see that,' I replied sarcastically. 'I'm doing my best to learn.'

'That's right,' he smiled, instantly mollified. 'Work hard, and you'll soon pick it all up. If you want to know anything . . .'

But I had ceased to listen. Becoming bored, I had strolled into the public bar, where I found a tall blue-eyed woman drinking a glass of Guinness by the till. She looked vaguely familiar.

'Good morning,' I said.

'Good morning,' said she. 'Are you Mr. Day?'

'Yes,' I smiled. 'We've met before, haven't we?'

'No; you're thinking of Mrs. Grainger. I'm her sister Daisy.'

'Oh! Do you often work here?'

'Whenever I can. I think it's fun.'

'You're not like your sister then; she doesn't like it.'

'Oh, she shouldn't be in this line: she ought to be in her old cake shop.'

'Ah! Cake shop . . .? She mentioned something to me about a cake shop.'

'She and Ron were saving up for one when they were engaged.'

'Oh, yes, and what happened?'

'Well, they got married before they'd saved enough. Then Mr. Marnes got the firm to give them this house. Lil was Mr. and Mrs. Marnes's cook, you know.'

'Oh, I see! That was rather decent of Mr. Marnes.'

'Maybe,' sniffed Daisy.

'Er—your sister been married long?'

'About eighteen months. Erm—I mean, two years.'

'Oh . . . ?' This seemed to me to be one of those cases of wheels within wheels. I made a rapid mental calculation, starting with Prebern's age. 'Mm—I see!'

Daisy flushed, and pretended to brush some dust from her sleeve. Apparently her sister was not so shy as Irene imagined. No wonder she could refuse with impunity to come downstairs and work in the bars. I wondered what Fatty Grainger thought about it all.

XII

OUR first Saturday at the Block and Anchor was some special day. Whit Monday, I think it was. No, it couldn't have been Whit Monday. Whit Saturday, perhaps, or a by-election day or something. I have forgotten now, but whatever it was, the hilarity born of the usual week-end generosity engendered by bulging pay packets was considerably accentuated by it. Even the old ladies in the private bar were gaily treating each other to nourishing stouts; and Irene and I, becoming pleasantly entangled in the general munificence, were soon in the happy condition known as slightly cheerio. Hardly had I made this interesting discovery (regarding myself) than Mr. Grainger drew me firmly to one side.

'Yes . . . ?' I said impatiently, my hands full of mugs, and wondering if I were about to be reprimanded. 'Er . . . yes ?'

'I'd better do the cellar today,' he muttered, with a side-long glance at the clock. 'You ain't got time to go down there today. See ?' There seemed to be something on his mind; but evidently he had not noticed my incipient insobriety.

'All right,' I said greatly relieved; for I felt I had passed the age when admonishment could be lightly endured; but at the same time I was annoyed at the idea of someone else doing my cellar. Tugging myself free, I walked impatiently towards the basin to wash the mugs.

'Just a minute,' he muttered clutching me again. 'You've no need to go down there at all today. See ?'

116

'All right,' I said.

'I'll do it all,' he added.

'Okay,' I snapped, and darted away.

'Half a minute.' He clutched my arm again. 'I'll do it this evening as well.'

'Right you are. I must get these mugs washed. You'll do it all day. I understand.'

'And you needn't go down there at all,' he persisted.

'Yes-yes,' I snapped. 'You've told me that already.' I turned to a customer. 'What is it, mate? Three halves and a mild-and-bitter? Righto. Coming up.'

That, for the moment, was the end of the matter, but during the evening session a bitter pump ran dry, and on trying the next one I found it had not been turned on in the cellar, and forgetful of my instructions, ran down and did it myself. Then I noticed that someone had stuck a funnel into a barrel of mild ale, and what's more, it was half full of water; and beside the barrel there were two beer buckets dripping with water!

'Careless!' I said to myself. 'Careless!' A brief examination showed there was a stoppage in the stem of the funnel; and after rapping on the head of the barrel with my knuckles to gauge its contents I climbed meditatively up the steps, to be met at the top by Fatty Grainger.

'What you been doing down there?'

'Turning on a new bitter.'

'Thought I told you I was doing the cellar today.'

'Sorry. I forgot.'

He went down the steps without another word, and I heard him stump across the cellar. As there was a stoppage in its stem the funnel must have been still half full of water. I imagined him searching unhappily for a length of wire, and wondering if I had seen the water, and if so, what I would do about it.

Presently he came up the steps and stood at the top of them staring miserably down at his feet. Then out of the corners of my eyes I saw him go into the saloon, and contrary to his usual custom—for he rarely drank intoxicants before the end of the day—pour himself a stiff glass of his wife's favourite tipple, gin and lemonade. He drank it as if he were doing a duty to his system, but it only served to deepen his gloom. A few minutes later, so Irene told me, he gave himself another, with the same effect.

The next time I noticed him he was standing just inside the saloon peering into the public bar at me, trying, I suppose, to divine by my expression whether I had noticed the water or not; but I was cheerio again by then, and with merry quips and jests, contributing considerably to the gaiety of the house. I had forgotten for the moment all about the water. My face was wreathed in smiles. Likewise, the faces of the customers. In fact, the only sombre visage in sight was the one belonging to Mr. Grainger, who grew steadily more morose as the evening progressed.

Occasionally he caught my eye, and I would wonder what on earth was the matter with the man, until, remembering the water, it occurred to me that he was merely wondering what I intended to do about it. Then, being in mellow mood, my sympathy surged towards him. That happened several times, but without comfort to Mr. Grainger, who— possibly because I was at such pains to avoid upsetting him by smiling—entirely misinterpreted my sympathetic expression, and mistook it for one of intense disgust. Which was rather sad in a way.

In the ordinary way, of course, a publican who waters his beer deserves no sympathy; but I could see his point of view. To my mind he was not a publican 'in the ordinary way'; he was merely a weak unbusinesslike man with an unscrupulous staff. Even his wife was—to put it mildly—no help to him; and somehow or other he had to make up for the drinks that went down her throat, and the throats of his staff, or lose his job. Looked at in that way, even the fact that he was completely unfit to be a manager had nothing to do with the case. To me he was just a poor little swine in a jam. I didn't like him, admittedly; but on the other hand, I didn't blame him.

After he had closed the house for the night he came sidling up to me.

'Come down in the cellar a moment, will you, Mr. Day?' he mumbled. 'I want to have a word with you.'

It was obvious what was coming, and a cosy chat in the cellar about watering beer was the last thing I wanted. I was tired and needed my dinner.

'There's rather a lot of clearing up to be done tonight,' I said, hedging.

'Never mind, I want to speak to you.'

'Hadn't I better wash these glasses first?' I persisted.

But he was on tenterhooks: he couldn't wait.

'You know, a man can't be honest in this line,' he blurted out, giggling foolishly to cover his embarrassment.

I decided to help him.

'No, I suppose he can't,' I mumbled commiseratingly, 'not with his staff guzzling all the profits.'

'No,' he said sadly.

I carried on with my glass-washing, and he stood nervously trying to rub a permanent stain from the counter

with a stubby forefinger. After a silence lasting several
seconds he glanced up at me, and I saw tears in his eyes.

He cleared his throat.

'A man's got to try and make it up somehow, or else get
the sack,' he mumbled.

'Mm,' I nodded sympathetically.

'And a fat lot they care whether you get the sack or not !'
he snorted.

'Wouldn't care a hang,' I agreed ; and then feeling I'd
had enough of the conversation, I made several bustling
journeys up and down the bar, collecting glasses and, tying
a cloth round my waist, splashed some of them carelessly into
the basin.

He took the hint, and went sadly into the saloon, brushing drips from his clothes on the way ; and finding his wife
mixing herself some gin and lemonade, he followed her
example.

XIII

WHILE we were cooking our dinner that evening I told Irene all about the water in the funnel and how Fatty had tried to inveigle me into the cellar for a quiet explanation.

'The silly little fool!' she exclaimed, plopping a chop into the frying-pan. 'He's too clumsy to be dishonest; he'll get caught one day.'

'He was this evening,' I grinned.

'I mean by someone who matters,' she smiled. 'You're not going to split on him, are you? You'll be a fool if you do.'

'Good lord, no!' I cried. 'Have a heart! I'm not a brewer's nark. Besides, I'm sorry for him. I don't think he's really dishonest; he's just frightened to death of losing his job. And I don't think he's as lazy as we thought either; I think he's just tired out.'

'And can you wonder!' she cried. 'With this great house on his hands, and no servants except old Kate who spends all her time scrubbing the patterns off the oilcloth, and a wife who does nothing except cook their own food and make the snacks, and a staff . . . well, look at his staff! He probably thinks we were sent from heaven to give him a rest.'

'So does Lil,' I grinned; 'though I do think she might cook our grub. Don't you?'

'Yes,' grimaced Irene; 'but I can see her point too. It's bad luck on us, of course, but I suppose she thinks Marnes has let her down; and she hates this house and has no intention of working in it.'

'Huh! I don't think Marnes has let her down. I think he's done her proud; he's fixed her up with a pub.'

'That's a man's point of view,' smirked Irene. 'Besides, she wanted a cake shop.'

'And in the meantime,' I laughed, 'old Fatty is wondering what the heck is the matter with her.'

'Shouldn't wonder,' laughed Irene. 'He's dumb enough; unless, of course . . . Oh! I don't know. We are a couple of scandalmongers! Did he put much water in the ale?'

'Can't say exactly, but there were two three-gallon buckets by the barrel, and the barrel was almost full. By the way, did the customers notice anything in your bar?'

'They kept it a dead secret if they did.'

'Same in mine. Not a grouse from anyone.'

'That's interesting,' smirked Irene.

'Yes,' I grinned, 'very; and I know what you're thinking. One can put six gallons of water into thirty gallons of ale without a customer knowing a thing about it.'

'Quite, darling. You'll make a publican one day. You see, even Fatty has taught us something. But he is taking a risk, isn't he?'

'Thinks it's worth it, I suppose. Thirty bob a bucket for water is not so bad, you know. Shouldn't have much trouble in keeping his stocks right at that rate. Why, with an honest staff he'd be on a dashed good wicket!'

'Until an excise officer walked in and tested the beer!' smiled Irene. 'They do that sometimes, don't they?'

'So I'm told; but I think he's allowing for that. I noticed him watching the clock this morning.'

'Watching the clock! Why?'

'He waited till twelve before he went into the cellar,' I grinned.

'What's that got to do with it?'

'Use your loaf, girl. Have you ever heard of a government wallah working between midday Saturday and Monday morning?'

'Oh—but one might one day.'

'And pigs might fly. This cabbage is done. Shall I strain it?'

'Yes, please, dear. Aren't you sick of cabbage? I am.'

At a quarter to one we put our dirty plates on the draining board and went up to bed.

XIV

DIRECTORS' day at the Block and Anchor was Wednesday, but after Irene and I came two Wednesdays passed without a visit, so on the morning of the third one there was quite an atmosphere behind the bars. We two were on tiptoe hoping to see the results of our good work appreciated; Rosie, and a sister of hers called Sandra who had come in to help that morning, were in bad tempers because Fatty wouldn't let them smoke; and he was more than ordinarily worried, because he was expecting a more than ordinarily thorough inspection to make up for the missed ones. Also, for some days past, regular customers had been remarking in unnecessarily loud voices on the improvements in the house since Irene and I arrived; and the directors, in Fatty's opinion, paid far too much attention to customers' remarks.

'Anyone would think the place was dirty before they came,' he muttered angrily to an old woman who was giving vent to some particularly pointed observations.

'And so it was,' declared her burly stevedore son; 'and so was yer bloomin' beer. Anyone can see as 'ow Perce ain't doing yer pipes no more; you can taste the difference.'

Mr. Grainger retired fuming to another bar.

'Couple o' new brooms!' he growled to Rosie. 'They'll find out when they get their own house.'

Then presently in walked Mr. Marnes; and it was obvious at once that Irene's surmise when we were first sent to the house was right. The directors had not expected us to stay; they thought the house would be too rough for us. Mr. Marnes was clearly amazed at the way we had knuckled down to the job. He congratulated us enthusiastically, and brushing aside with an impatient gesture a tentative remark by Fatty, to the effect that we were quite good at obeying his instructions, scrutinized the cabinets, the shelves under the counters, the pewter, and the glasses; and then sampled the beer.

'Very good,' he said. 'Very good. I can see you have both been working hard.' He went down into the cellar, and returning some twenty minutes later, congratulated us again; and added, 'I take it you have been doing the cellar, Mr. Day?'

'Yes, sir,' I replied.

'Very good indeed,' he said. 'Yes—I can see you have both been working hard.' He smiled at Irene. 'Do you like it here?'

'No,' she said.

'Eh! You don't . . . ?' There was a twinkle in his eye.

'No,' she said; 'I don't like it here at all.'

He laughed.

'Well, there's one thing about you and your husband, you always speak your minds.' (We supposed by that, that he was referring to our request for a move from the Gorget Hotel.) 'However,' he added, 'it may not be for long.'

'Thank you,' said Irene pointedly.

He smiled again, and turned to the now scowling Mr. Grainger.

'Can't stop today,' he said shortly. 'Shan't bother with the books. Good morning.' With that, he strode out to his car.

The next morning, to everyone's surprise, the three directors arrived and inspected the house; and afterwards Mr. Kent took Irene and me aside.

'We're sending you to another house as soon as we've made the necessary arrangements,' he said. 'We're very pleased with your work here, and we're—er—rather hoping your period of training will not be quite so long as is usual; but we think Mrs. Day should—er—have more experience of the catering side, so we're sending you to our White Lark. There's a good lunch trade there; and you will concentrate on the kitchen, will you, Mrs. Day? And you, Mr. Day, had better go thoroughly into the accounts. I'll have a word with the manager. By the way, how are you getting on with the tills, Mrs. Day? Getting better at them?'

'I beg your pardon . . . ?' said Irene flushing.

I saw an angry glint in her eye, and felt myself flush. So the Lawsons had mentioned that ten-shilling note after all, had they!

'She's all right at the tills, sir,' I snapped.

'Good? Good? They were awkward at first, I expect. Well, thank you both for what you've done. You'll be hearing from us in a day or two. By the way, I think you'll find the customers at the Lark a little pleasanter than they are here.' He smiled at Irene, patted her shoulder in a fatherly manner that made her feel about twelve years old, and went upstairs to join his colleagues who were inspecting the accounts.

'Well, I'm damned!' she said when he'd gone. 'So those stinking Lawsons told them I was no good on the tills!'

'The ruddy swines!' I growled. 'I wish I'd sloshed him now.' I went fuming back to my bar.

A few minutes later Fatty Grainger came waddling into the saloon, beaming and rubbing his hands together.

'You look pleased with yourself,' remarked Irene.

'I am,' he said. 'Always pleased when the directors have gone.'

'Oh? Why? Don't you like them?'

'Huh!' snorted Fatty.

'I rather care for them,' smiled Irene.

'Huh! You'll find out one day. You wait till you get your own house. Still, they weren't bad this morning. They tell me they're shifting you two to the Lark.'

'Yes. Do you know where it is?'

'Gladstone Park, between Fenwick and Greenheath.'

'Oh! Our flat is at Greenheath!' She came running into the public bar. 'D'you know the White Lark at Gladstone Park, darling?'

'No,' said I. 'Is that the one we're going to?'

'Yes.'

'I say, what a bit o' luck. We shall be able to live at home if we don't like it. It's only a tuppenny bus ride.'

XV

THE next Saturday I had a letter from the firm saying we were to report for duty at the White Lark on the following Wednesday evening; and about half-way through the morning session I took it into the saloon and showed it to Fatty.

'Oh, yes,' said he, not troubling to read it. 'Head Office just been on the phone. Wednesday evening at the White Lark.'

'That's right. When can we go? We'd rather like a couple of days off.'

'You can go now if you like. I was just going to tell you.'

'This afternoon, you mean?'

'No; now. You've got a flat where you can stay, haven't you?'

'Yes, but we'll wait till the end of the session.'

'No, don't bother,' he smiled. 'You go now. We're not too busy for a Saturday morning, and we got plenty o' help coming in this evening.'

'Well, that's very kind of you, Mr. Grainger, but—er—we'll finish the session.'

'Oh, no we won't,' snapped Irene, drying her hands on a glass-cloth. 'I'm off. Come on, goof!' She flung the cloth on a hook and raised the flap. 'Coming?'

'Half a sec, I——'

She started for the door marked *Private*, so I followed her.

'You are a fool,' she said when we were going upstairs. 'Can't you see he's just dying to get into the cellar and water the beer?'

'Oh! I never thought of that,' I grinned. 'I was thinking about the serving.'

'That's his worry. He's got Rosie and Sandra in the saloon, and Daisy in your bar; and I think that couple who were here when we first came are coming in this evening. He'll manage. He never worried about us. You nip out and find a taxi while I pack, and we'll be home by one. Then we can have lunch somewhere, and do some shopping, and have four days in our own flat.

'Okay, my beautiful.'

A few minutes later we were lolling back in a hired car.

'Isn't it fun,' chuckled Irene. 'One minute we're pulling up mild-and-bitters for the great unwashed, and the next we're fizzing across London in a Daimler like Lord and Lady Muck.'

We arrived at the flat in holiday mood, to be greeted directly we opened the door by our own familiar atmosphere. Everything belonged to us, and looked pleased to see us. A novel, left open on the arm of a chair, seemed to say, 'Here I am, waiting for you.' Cigarettes lay like hiding children in the box on the mantelpiece. Not a thing had been touched since we left. There were even some friendly crocks still soaking in the sink.

'I feel as if I'd never been away, don't you?' cried Irene.

'Yes,' I said; 'and everything smells of us.'

She sniffed.

'So it does! I suppose every home has its own smell really. Change from beer, isn't it? Think we'll ever get used to the smell of beer?'

'More likely cease to notice it after a time. I can hardly smell this place now.'

E

She sniffed again.

'Funny! It's wearing off. What an extraordinary thing!'

'It isn't really. You only noticed it because you'd been away. But that's enough about stinks. What about a snort?'

'Yes. Mix a couple of gin slings; then we'll really know we're at home. Shall I see if I can find some tins? You don't want to go out for lunch, do you? It's fun being back, isn't it!'

'Yes,' I smiled; 'you get the grub going. I'll mix the drinks.'

We had a very pleasant afternoon, starting with an impromptu meal consisting of two tins of Irene's eternal sardines, digestive biscuits and jam; then I lit the boiler, while Irene lit the bedroom fire and draped the bedclothes round it; and after that we did the shopping.

At five o'clock we ran out of money, and then remembered it was Saturday afternoon and the banks were closed; so I telephoned Enid, who came to the rescue and later on drove us to Town, where the three of us had a cheery dinner and enjoyed a delightful comedy that had been slanged by all the critics, and Enid drove us back to the flat.

'Coming up for a nightcap?' Irene asked her.

'You bet,' she said, 'if it's one of your funny Malay ones.'

'You mix them,' I said to Irene, 'while I find my cheque book and settle with Enid for the cash she's lent us.'

'No hurry about that,' smiled Enid.

'Better do it now,' I said, diving a hand into a trouser pocket and bringing it out full of coppers and sixpences. 'Would you like some of this back now?'

'No,' she smiled. 'I've enough to last till Monday. Anyway, you only owe me two-thirds. I'll pay my share. Don't suppose you've much left, have you?'

I searched all my pockets.

'By Jove, you're right!' I glanced at Irene. 'I say, sweetheart, we've spent about a fortnight's wages this evening. Where the heck has it all gone to?'

Enid laughed.

'The sooner you two get a pub of your own the better. You can't do much on ten pounds a week nowadays, you know.'

'So it seems,' I said. 'But still, we don't go out every night.'

'You can't go out once a month on ten pounds a week if you spend money the way you did this evening. I don't know why you don't let me buy you a p——'

'Now-now, sister! None o' that. We're not going to sponge on you.' I turned to Irene. 'We'll have a quiet day tomorrow: go down and see the cats, and have a nice walk in the country, eh?'

'Right you are,' she said; 'and on Monday we'll come down to earth and the one-and-ninepennies.'

'That's the style!' I grinned, absentmindedly brushing some dust from my trousers. 'I say, hasn't everything got dusty while we've been away! We must get a char in.'

'You can fix that when you get to the White Lark,' said Enid.

'Or we can slip over and do it ourselves,' I suggested.

'Thanks,' snorted Irene. 'You may if you like; I shall have quite enough cleaning to do at the White Lark without coming here to——'

'Oh, quite!' I said quickly. 'Sorry. I apologize.'

'What will you do with this place when you get your management?' Enid asked.

'Let it, I suppose,' said Irene. 'Seems a pity, with our good furniture, but the cash will be useful. We can take the best stuff with us, of course.'

'Don't forget you can pick and choose your tenants these days, thanks to the housing shortage. I'll keep my ears open if you like. I won't say anything to anyone, but you know . . . !'

'Thanks, dear, that would help.'

'Right you are. Well, children, it's time I went home to bed.'

XVI

IRENE and I spent Sunday morning at the cattery playing
with Rubbertumi and Kinkiboo, had a sandwiches-and-
beer lunch and went for a long country walk, and returning
to Greenheath soon after opening time, dined at our local
and went early to bed. The next day, feeling tired after our
unwonted outdoor exercise, we stayed at home lazing and
listening to the radio, and darning socks, and sorting out
clothes and so forth; all very domesticated. It was an
enjoyable change.

On Tuesday morning we caught a bus to Gladstone Park
to pay the usual courtesy call before reporting for duty at
the White Lark, and to our surprise found it rather a
common district. I say to our surprise because it was so
close to Greenheath, which considers itself somewhat
exclusive; and we were disappointed too, after Mr. Kent's
remark about the pleasanter customers. It was not as bad as
Basin Lane, of course, but all the same we would have been
even more disappointed if we had been going there as
managers; though the White Lark itself was nice enough.
It was a large ramshackle building, not too attractive from
the outside, but quite comfortable inside, with cosy well-
furnished bars, and large fireplaces. Mr. and Mrs. Handen,
the manager and his wife, were the old-fashioned type,
fortyish and rotund, and obviously appreciative of the
goods they sold. They gave us a welcome such as we had
visualized, but had not received, at either of the other two
houses; though I suppose Fatty Grainger had done his
best, but he just wasn't the type. Perhaps we had expected

too much, but we certainly had anticipated a more friendly spirit within the trade than we had experienced so far. In fact, we were beginning to wonder if the happy-go-lucky atmosphere normally associated with public houses was not confined entirely to the customers' side of the counter; which was hardly a happy thought.

Our welcome at the White Lark, however, made up for a lot.

'Ho!—so you're Mr. and Mrs. Day, are you!' beamed Mr. Handen leaning across the counter to shake hands. 'Coming to learn the trade, are you? Ha! you'll soon change your minds. Maggie! Here's Mr. and Mrs. Day.'

'Oh, don't put them off, Harold,' smiled his wife, sailing along behind the bar and shaking hands with both of us at once. 'They'll find out soon enough. It's not a bad life if you don't weaken. How are you? When are you coming?'

'We were told to come tomorrow evening,' I smiled.

'All right, come along about five, then we can tell you the prices before we open at half past. I'll have your room ready. Nice double bed, I expect you'd like, Mrs. Day, eh?'

'Well—er—we rather fancy singles,' replied Irene.

'Oh, so you prefer singles! Just like me and the guv. Hear that, Harold? They like single beds, the same as we do. All right, you can have them. Come and see your room, dear. I expect our old pot-and-pans want a word together.' She lifted the flap and mothered Irene into the residential part of the building via the inevitable door marked *Private.*

Mr. Handen winked an eye at me.

'Have a drink?'

'Thanks. I'd like a bitter, please.'

He tossed a coin to the barmaid.

'Two bitters, Kath.'

Kath pulled them up and put them on the counter with the change.

'Good health!' said Mr. Handen, raising his glass.

'Good health,' said I, taking a sip, and not forgetting to roll it round my tongue before swallowing. Then carefully placing my glass where it would catch the light, I quizzed it professionally, and smiled at my new boss. 'Nice drop o' bitter!' I remarked appreciatively.

'Good health!' said Mr. Handen, raising his glass

He beamed.

'It's looked after,' he affirmed. 'I reckon you won't get a better drop in south-east London.'

'I reckon you won't,' I agreed heartily.

That went down very well with the guv.

'Know anything about cellar work?' he inquired.

'Well, I've only been in the business a few weeks.'

He smiled his appreciation of that modest reply, and I felt I had made a hit.

'Not much in it,' he observed, giving me a friendly pat on the back of my hand, 'as long as you use your head, and aren't too greedy. That's where chaps lets themselves down. You see, you got to make up your mind whether you're going to increase your turnover or save on the farthings—because you can't do both—but the directors won't see that; they go on percentage per barrel. It depends on whether you owns or manages the house, see? But I'll show you all that. F'rinstance, if you sells five pounds' worth o' beer including the swipes for a hundred shillings, you're one o' the crowd; but if you sells *two* lots—*without* the swipes—for ninety-eight shillings each, you're on the up-and-up. See what I mean? You're getting all the custom. And you can afford to chuck the swipes away. But you forget all you've been taught, and do what I tell you while you're here. Then you can do what you like when you get your own house. Savvy?'

'Yes.'

'Well, don't forget. Because I'm proud o' my bitter; that's what makes your name—and you don't want to muck about with your mild too much, either. All mild-ale drinkers ain't dumb, though there's many as thinks they are. I can guess what you've been taught, see?'

'All right,' I smiled. 'I understand.' I was beginning to like this chap.

'Care to see the cellar?' he asked. 'You needn't if you don't want to,' he added with a smile. 'You'll see enough of it when you get here.'

'I'd like to very much,' I said.

'Come on then.'

The cellar was entered by a trapdoor in the private bar. He heaved it up and hooked it against the wall, and then with much puffing and blowing, lowered himself down the ladder. I followed, to find a cellar very much like the one at the Gorget Hotel, only larger.

'It ain't as clean as I'd like it,' he remarked; 'but it's the rotten staff you get nowadays. The more you pay 'em the less they do. First you tell 'em what you want done, then you have to go and do most of it yourself. After that the directors come along and ask you why you ain't done it properly. The directors don't know what it is nowadays, you see. When they was keeping pubs themselves, before the war, the staff had to earn their wages or else they got the sack; but you can't sack 'em these days. Why, you can't hardly get any to sack. Working clarss, they call themselves. Blimey! it's the managers what does all the work. We're the bloomin' working clarss. You'll find that out, Mr. Ray, when you get your own house.'

'Yes, I've found it out already,' I smiled. 'By the way, the name's Day, not Ray.'

'Oh, Dray, is it! Sorry. People generally call me Hendon; but it ain't, it's Handen. *And* there's a aitch to it. You Conservative?'

'Eh!' I exclaimed, missing the trend of the question. 'D'you mean in politics?'

'Yes. Are you a Conservative?'

'Yes, I am.'

'So am I. I hates the working clarss. And can you blame me! I have to do all me own cellar work here. If I pay a cellarman he mucks up the bitter, drinks half the mild, and then I have to go down and clear up after him; not that anyone pays me for doing his job. But you daren't mention that in the public bar. All socialists and communists in there. They expect some blighter called "They" to do everything for 'em. *They* ought to do this, and *They* ought to do that. Who the hell *They* is heaven only knows, but he's got his work cut out, accordin' to them. Shall we go up?'

'Righto.'

He started to struggle up the ladder.

'Better wait till I get to the top,' he puffed. 'This ladder won't hold both of us. What do you go? Fifteen stone?'

'Not quite. About fourteen.'

'My missis goes nearly that,' he chuckled. 'Sixteen me. Shut the trap, will you? You can bend better than what I can. Shan't be sorry when you're here to do the runnin' up and down instead o' me.'

I couldn't help smiling at the idea of his sixteen stone running up and down a ladder.

'Care for a drink?' I asked when we were back in the saloon.

'Thanks, I'll have a bitter with you. Kath! Two bitters, please. Did they teach you much at the houses where you've been?'

'Not a lot,' I grinned.

'No—they don't!' he snorted. 'Nobody never taught me nothing. Frightened I'd pinch their job after they'd taught me, I suppose. I'll learn you the cellar an' the books. The books ain't much, and you'll pick up most o' the rest if you're ever going to be any good. My old woman will show your missis the catering. I don't know nothing about that. It don't pay, anyway.'

'Oh?' I said in surprise. 'How's that?'

'Can't in a house this size, unless you do all the work yourself. All goes in wages. All right if you're doing a hundred or so lunches a day; but it's a dead loss here. We only do lunches to please the licensing magistrates. Then we count as caterers, see? And that's one up against the temperance crowd.'

'That's interesting,' I remarked.

' 'Tis if you're thinking o' getting a tenancy or buying a house,' he said with a wink. 'It's all a matter o' wages. You can work it out yourself. Comes different in each house, see? But, mind you, the brewers like you to do lunches. Keeps 'em right with the temperance crowd, like I said just now; not to mention the licensing magistrates who happen to be grocers, and sell wines and spirits *et cetera* themselves. Wonderful lot o' grocers there are on the bench. Don't suppose you've ever had anything to do with magistrates, eh? They're a rum lot.'

'I've an aunt who's one.'

'Have you! Is she a grocer?'

'No.'

'What's she do? Anything? Or just married?'

'Owns a bit o' property.'

'Ah! I bet there's a grocer's shop amongst it. Otherwise, what's she on the bench for? Hallo! here's your missis.'

Irene and Mrs. Handen were just coming back by the door marked *Private*.

'Oh, there you are!' cried Irene. 'Ready to go, dear?'

'Yes, I'm ready, dear.'

We said good-bye and started for home.

'What do you think of them?' I asked, as we settled our-selves on the top of a bus. 'Not bad, eh?'

'Mrs. Handen is sweet; she's an absolute pet, but I don't think I shall learn a lot from her.'

'Oh? Why?'

'She doesn't know a thing about catering. She couldn't answer a single question; didn't even know how many lunches they serve. Whenever I asked her anything she just said "Oh, Cook'll tell you that." As far as I can make out, the cook runs the whole house except the cellar.'

'Well, that's a weight off your mind,' I grinned. 'It can't be too difficult if the cook does it all.'

'I hope not,' said Irene doubtfully. 'What's he like?'

'Seems a good chap. I think he's going to be helpful. And he's genuinely proud of his draught beer. That's a good sign. Is the bedroom all right?'

'Absolutely luxurious, my dear. There's a three-foot-by-four mat in the middle of the oilcloth, a wardrobe as well as a nail in the door, and she has promised to change the double bed for two single ones. Oh, and there's a bentwood chair.'

'I say! we shall feel like a couple of film stars. What shall we do this afternoon? Go for a walk?'

'Oh, darling, I'm still stiff after our Sunday walk. You know, we've hardly been out since we started this job. Aren't you stiff?'

'Yes, a bit, especially my game leg; though we only did seven or eight miles. You wouldn't think we'd notice it after being on our feet all day for so long—and me an ex-planter used to ten and twelve miles a day!'

'One uses different muscles for standing.'

'Yes—but I could do with some exercise, all the same. Let's go for a row at Richmond; that'll loosen up my barrel-lifting muscles, and you can row or sit and look beautiful, whichever you like.'

'I'll sit and look beautiful, thanks; but what about lunch?'

'Have it there.'

'Too late. There's no Tube from here.'

'Oh. Well, let's hire a car.'

'Darling, d'you think we ought! All the way to Richmond?'

'Dash it! we're on holiday.'

Irene laughed.

'Yes. Let's then. We'll get one at the garage on the heath. Have you enough money?'

'We can call at the bank.'

'Come on then, we get off at the next stop. After all, we must take exercise sometimes.'

'Of course!' I agreed. 'We can't potter about behind bars all our lives and never have any proper exercise. We'd get ill.'

'Of course we would,' snorted Irene.

So having thus justified the expense, we hired an ancient but very comfortable Rolls-Royce, and embarked for Richmond via the bank. When we arrived, half asleep after the long ride, the chauffeur asked for further directions.

'Oh, drive us to some nice place for lunch,' I yawned.

Impressed by my lordly command he drove us to a place about the size of Buckingham Palace.

'Gosh!' I muttered to Irene. 'This must be about the slap-upest pub in the town.'

'Never mind,' she said, 'we're on holiday.'

So in holiday spirit I settled with the chauffeur, to the latter's eminent satisfaction, and conducted Irene to the cocktail bar.

It was a nice bar, with some pleasant people about, so we dallied there awhile and enjoyed some very delectable cocktails before pushing off to the dining-room; and then, as the menu looked pretty good, I thought it should not be disgraced by inferior wine. Irene agreed. But the coffee that followed was the usual hotel stuff, so we ignored that and had half a bottle of excellent port, of which, needless to say, I consumed a man's share. By then we had lost all sense of tiredness, though Irene still didn't feel like rowing—as a matter of fact, she doesn't like rowing—but I felt fit enough to row the *Yarmouth Belle* across the Channel to Boulogne, and said so; and presently we were tripping (in more senses than one) into a skiff. But we soon had enough of that. After trying to race a motor-boat and then a pleasure steamer I became overcome by an unaccountable shortness of breath, and Irene began to natter about the shape of her seat and a pain in the back, or a pain in her seat and the shape of the boat; she seemed in some doubt about it all. Anyway, she said she wanted to get out. Then we discovered that the steamer and the motor-boat had been heading downstream, and it took me nearly two hours to row back to the boat-house. By that time the holiday spirit had evaporated, so we dropped into the second slap-upest pub in the town to remove a peculiar feeling of depression that had taken its place. We managed to do that very successfully. In fact, when we eventually arrived back at the flat, at a quarter past twelve, we were in the gayest of moods again, though minus the best part of another fortnight's joint salary.

'Now, what about dinner?' said Irene bustling somewhat unsteadily into the kitchen. 'What do you fancy, darling?'

'Well, is there anything to fancy?' I asked.

'Must be, I should think,' she replied, flinging open the larder door. 'Lessavalook. We got some cornflakes. Oh! and some spiced beef. And there's some hashed beef! That's a swine to open. Oh! and pickled onions. I forgot these. Why, we've got practically everything! And plenty of tinned peas. They're easy to cook, and where the hell did these prunes come from! We never eat prunes. We don't like prunes. Does Enid eat prunes? D'you think she left them here? Surely not! Eh? Does she?'

'I don't know.'

'What! Don't you know if your sister likes prunes?'

'Oh, shut up about prunes, girl, and find me the tin-opener.'

'Well, I'm not going to eat the beastly things. I don't even like custard. Here's the tin-opener. What shall I do with the hashed spice? Make a stew?'

'Leave it to me, sweetheart. Go and mix some drinks.'

'All ri'; but don't you think I ought to practise my cooking?'

'No; go away. I want something to eat.'

At about half past one we put down our knives and forks and having dined in the kitchen, bundled the crocks into the sink—absentmindedly leaving them for a Lily Grainger or a Kate to wash in the morning—and went to bed.

'Not a bad day, cocky!' breathed Irene as I switched out the bed light.

'Not so bad, sweetheart.'

'Shan't mind keeping a pub if we can do this now and again.'

'No—perfectly all ri'. Pleasant dreams, darling.'

'Good ni', Cook—I mean cock.'

XVII

AT five minutes to five the next evening we were waiting, with our suitcases at our feet, outside the White Lark. Presently we heard footsteps coming down the stairs.

'That's Maggie,' said Irene.

I nodded, and the door opened.

'Ah, there you are!' smiled Mrs. Handen. 'Would you like to run up and put your things away? You've got time; we're just going to chalk the prices up for you. *Harold! Here they are!* You know where your room is, Mrs. D. Take your old man up and then come down to the saloon.'

A few minutes later we were being shown round behind the bars; and at half past five Mr. Handen took the keys from the rack and tossed them to the potman.

'Okay, Alf.'

Mrs. Handen passed round a packet of cigarettes, and the four of us stood talking at the end of the counter.

At a quarter to six the first customer drifted in, an old woman with a shopping basket containing two empty stout bottles.

'Oh dear! first again,' she simpered. 'I don't know what you'll think of me. Guinness, dear, please.'

Mrs. Handen poured it out, and exchanged the empty bottles for full ones without being asked, and turned to Irene.

'We don't get many in before seven. Hardly worth opening really. But we're generally pretty busy after that. The bar staff come in at half past six. No need to pay them for standing about.'

'I hate this time o' the day,' grumbled Mr. Handen. 'Too slow for me.' He took hold of my arm. 'Come down in the cellar and I'll show you how we work the bitter here.'

Nothing loath, I followed him down the rickety ladder, and spent the next few minutes listening to a most interesting monologue on the art of beer-keeping. His methods turned out to be almost identical with those of Mr. Lawson at the Gorget Hotel; but unlike that semi-moron, he knew how to impart his knowledge, and explain the reasons for the various processes; which, of course, made his little lecture not only interesting but very useful. Realizing that at last I was being taught something, I thanked him gratefully.

'That's all right,' he beamed. 'But you seem to have picked the job up already, as far as I can see. Like to take over the cellar?'

'Very much indeed,' I smiled.

'Okay,' he said. 'I'll keep an eye on you for a few days, of course. You mustn't mind that.' He pulled out a carton of cigarettes. 'Fag?'

'Thanks.'

We lit up.

'Think you're going to like this line?'

'Yes, I think so.'

'It ain't a bad life in some ways,' he remarked, making himself comfortable on an upturned cask. 'You're your own master—up to a point; but it's a tie. Sixteen hours a day, with the rotten staff you get nowadays; and when you do get a day off it's generally on your own. You happily married? You look it.'

'Yes, thanks,' I grinned.

'So am I,' he sighed; 'and that's the trouble. You're lucky

if you get out with your missis once a month, with this firm, and it ain't enough. Still, p'r'aps it won't be for ever.'

I gave him a keen look.

'Thinking of applying for a tenancy?'

'You never know,' he grinned. 'My brother's got one. Not this brewery either.' He winked his eye. 'A word in the right place, eh? But that's between you and me.'

'Oh, rather!' I exclaimed, thinking him somewhat loquacious considering he hardly knew me. I wondered if he had had a couple before opening time, and concluded he had.

He continued:

'Me and my brother could work our days off between us then; and he's got a son what stands in for him occasionally. He gets plenty o' time off; got a government job.'

'That's useful,' I murmured. 'But what do tenants do about days off when they haven't a brother who is a publican, or a son working for the government? And how do they manage for summer holidays?'

'Ah! That's a problem.'

I agreed; but felt that as far as I was concerned it was one for the distant future. Meanwhile, in the almost deserted saloon, Irene and Mrs. Handen were discussing catering.

'What do you want to work in the kitchen for?' inquired Mrs. Handen with a puzzled frown.

'Mr. Kent told me to,' replied Irene.

'But you can cook, can't you?'

'Of course; but I've never carved for a lot of people.'

'Oh, that's the cook's job,' snorted Mrs. Handen. 'She can't pack up directly the food is ready to serve.'

'Don't you ever work in the kitchen?'

'Me! Not likely! Except on directors' days, of course; because they like to see you messing about in there. They think you're supervising. You see, they think things are like they was before the war; but you can't go supervising your cook these days, my dear. You'd never see her next morning if you tried that game. All you'd see would be a rude note telling you where to send her insurance card.'

'Oh,' said Irene despondently. 'But what happens if a director asks how I'm getting on with the catering?'

Mrs. Handen burst out laughing.

'Why! you tell him you're doing fine, of course. So will I. I'll say you're as good as me. You may work in the kitchen if you like; but I warn you, if Cook gets annoyed and leaves, you'll have to do all the cooking yourself till I get another one.'

'Oh,' said Irene again.

'Of course, you can go into the kitchen on directors' mornings, and welcome. Cook'll understand that. She'll play up to you, and ask questions, and that.'

'Oh gosh!' cried Irene.

'You needn't be afraid,' laughed Mrs. Handen. 'You won't have to answer them. You just say "Oh, I'll leave that to you, Cook; I can trust your judgment." That'll put you in with the director, see? He'll think you've got everything in hand, and are just treating her tactful.'

'I see,' said Irene doubtfully.

'And then you fuss about looking into things,' continued Mrs. Handen. 'Have a peep into the steamer, for instance. See what I mean? It's just a technique. And if the steamed pudding looks a little worse than usual that day, you say "Oh, what a lovely steamed pudding, Cook!"—and slam the door shut before the director can poke his nose in. That keeps you right with the cook, you see; and if she knows her stuff, like this one does, she'll upset a cup o' gravy, or a drop o' custard or something, on the floor by his shoes, and he'll think he knocked it over when he hopped back from the steamer door; and that puts *her* right with *you*—and you're all happy. Get the idea? We all work together when a director is here.'

'But what about him?' laughed Irene. 'Doesn't he get in a temper when his shoes are messed up?'

'You don't wait to find out, dear. You open the door into the lounge and shout at the top of your voice "What?... Wanted on the phone?... Righto!" Then you dash upstairs, and smoke a cigarette till he's gone down into the cellar with the guv. Directors like to think you're rushed off your feet. It's a very good line to take. They imagine they're getting value for your salary. Oh no! he doesn't get in a temper.'

'When is directors' day here?'

'Thursdays. I'll give you an apron, dear, but you needn't put it on till he comes. Just splash a drop of gravy on it and keep it handy. If he catches you in here you can pretend you've just popped in to tell me something. Keep your wits about you; that's all you've got to do. Don't worry about the catering. Like a drink? We'll be busy presently.'

'Thank you. May I have a Guinness?'

'Righto. And give me one too, will you?'

When Irene had poured them out she glanced involuntarily at the till.

'That's all right, dear,' said Mrs. Handen reading her thoughts. 'I'll fix that presently. You see, I drink gin with the customers.'

'Oh, quite!' muttered Irene, wondering what drinking gin with the customers had to do with paying for Guinnesses; but she soon found out.

A man came in just then and ordered a double whisky; and when Mrs. Handen served him he asked her if she would take something.

'Thanks,' she said, 'I'll have a gin'; and pouring herself a double one, she gave him his change, and raised her glass.

'No water?' he inquired, reaching for the carafe.

'Not for me!' she laughed. 'You know I never believe in spoiling the stuff. Here's how!' She took a tiny sip, and when he wasn't looking put the rest carefully at the back of a shelf under the counter, with a half wink at Irene.

Irene said nothing, but like the parrot, thought a lot.

Just then Mr. Handen and I came up from the cellar, discussing accounts.

'Yes, I'll show you them sometime,' he was saying over his shoulder. 'You don't have to worry about 'em; it only takes a few minutes. There's nothing to 'em really; they're only returns. You see, all the invoices except the catering ones go direct to Head Office. They keep all the real accounts.'

'Then how d'you know what profit the house is making?' I asked.

'You don't,' he smiled. 'They take good care o' that; but you soon find out if it ain't enough. If you knew what profit the house was making you'd be after a tenancy yourself,' he chuckled. 'Anyway, you'd always be worrying them for a rise.' My question seemed to amuse him vastly.

Still chuckling, he accepted a gin from a customer, diluted it with a few drops of bitter beer, and tossed it off; and then went into secret confabulation with his wife. She seemed just as amused.

At half past six a barmaid came in and went into the kitchen to change her outdoor shoes for comfortable working ones. Ten minutes later two more barmaids came in and did the same. At a quarter to seven Mr. Handen stalked through the lounge and opened the kitchen door.

'Come on, you girls!'

'Okay, guv, just coming,' they chorused; and a moment later out they came, and noses in air, filed into the saloon, to find Mrs. Handen waiting for them with the flap ready raised.

While they were dispersing to their places Mr. Handen switched on the lights. Then the house began to fill, and he fussed from bar to bar, serving whenever there was any congestion of custom, and accepting gins and beers impartially as they were offered; while his wife stationed herself directly in front of the till, where she remained for the rest of the evening, accepting and drinking Guinnesses, accepting and pretending to drink gins, and completely blocking the traffic behind the counter every time she bent down to add to her store of gin underneath it.

At eight o'clock she told Irene we could go and have our supper.

'Where do we have it?' Irene asked.

'In the kitchen, through the lounge there. You'll find plenty of food in the fridge.'

'Righto,' said Irene peeping under the counter and noting a row of six gins. Hm! No fool, our Maggie! She looked into the private bar, where I was working. 'Come on, cocky, it's supper time.'

I followed her into the kitchen; and we cooked ourselves a tasty fry-up in a pan big enough to take a dozen eggs at a time, and ate it at the high preparation table, which was so high that it came nearly up to our chins. It was meant, of course, to be used by people standing at it to prepare food, not as a dining table. We came to hate that preparation table. It was so uncomfortable. We even tried to eat standing at it, but that was worse still.

However, during our meal Irene told me about Mrs. Handen's gins.

'Good lord!' I snorted. 'That's a bit hot. I didn't think she was that kind of woman.'

'Come off it, Mr. Unctuous,' sneered Irene. 'It's time you dropped your pukka sahib nonsense, my boy, and became a pukka publican. They have to earn their living the same as the Lawsons and the Graingers, and anybody else. And I expect the firm expects it, otherwise why do they pay such lousy salaries?'

I shut up. This was a side of Irene's character that was quite new to me. I was rather shocked.

On her way back to work after supper she had another peep under the counter, and saw two more gins there, and a partly consumed Guinness. There was also a Guinness on the counter; for Mrs. Handen, as we soon discovered, never refused a drink on principle. She considered free drinks were legitimate perks. When customers could afford it she had gin for her hoard; otherwise, she had Guinness, which she drank. Mr. Handen did much the same, except that he didn't save any drinks; he drank all that came his way.

By nine o'clock that evening (or on any other evening, for that matter) they could easily be recognized as that oft-described couple, the genial host and hostess. In other words, the guv and his missis were cheerfully blotto; not swaying about or slurring their words, or anything like that, but even the dullest of customers could make them burst into laughter with the feeblest repartee. Nevertheless, they were still working hard, he by keeping an eye on the tills and the draught beer, and seeing that customers were not kept waiting; and she by maintaining with laughter and light patter the proper party spirit, and also by accumulating under the counter rows of gins for re-sale the next day for the benefit of the aforementioned genial host and hostess. They made an excellent team.

At ten-thirty Time was called, and as the last customer drifted unwillingly into the street in a haze of tobacco smoke, Alf the potman clanged the grids behind him and closed the house. Mr. Handen tested all the locks and bolts. Barmaids set to, washing glasses and mopping up; and Mrs. Handen, with the aid of a little copper funnel, re-bottled the gin she had collected under the counter.

As soon as the staff had gone Mr. and Mrs. Handen started to cash up, and Irene and I offered to help.

'All right,' said Mrs. Handen, giving Irene some pint mugs filled with notes. 'You stop here with me and count these. Your old man can help the guv.' Then she reached behind the till for a glass containing some money and a pencil and paper.

'What's that?' Irene asked.

'I'll explain it to you one day,' replied Mrs. Handen casually. 'Have a Guinness, dear : and you'd better give your old man a pint at the same time.'

'Thank you,' said Irene.

Mrs. Handen emptied the glass she had taken from behind the till, and counted the money, and then spent several minutes doing what appeared to Irene to be higher mathematics with the pencil and paper. Presently she swept the money back into the glass, and shouted into the next bar.

'Thirty-six and ninepence in the kitty, Harold.'

'Good for you, Maggie ! How much today ?'

'Nine singles and three doubles; and one old fool bought me a double whisky!'

'Goodo! Averaging well, ain't we!'

Irene, who had been taking all this in, continued with her counting; but she found it hard to keep her mind on the work. Thirty-six and ninepence in the kitty! She supposed that was the money taken for yesterday's gin. And nine singles and three doubles, and a double whisky today. That was too much for her to work out in her head, but she liked the sound of it. All that gained quite honestly too; or was it? She could work that out. Someone buys you a drink; then naturally, that's your drink; and you sell it, and that's your money. Well, that was all right! Because if you hadn't accepted it nobody would have bought it; so the firm didn't suffer. Even Bill, with his old-school-tie conscience, couldn't grumble at that. But perhaps she had better think it over a bit before pressing the point. Bill was a trifle snooty at supper. But, by gosh! it was hard work. Old Maggie hadn't stopped talking and joking for a second the whole evening. But still, thirty-six and ninepence, and all you wanted to drink on top of that! And all those doubles and singles to sell the next day. What the heck!

'Counted those notes yet?' Mrs. Handen asked.

'Oh! Nearly finished. Let me see, where was I! Fifty-one fifty-two fifty-three. Shan't be long now. Fifty-four fifty-five fifty-six. . . .'

XVIII

THE next morning we were up at half past seven; and in the absence of orders from either of the Handens, I went down and worked in the cellar, while Irene cleaned mirrors and dusted cabinets in the bars. At nine o'clock Mrs. Handen wandered into the saloon with a cup of tea in her hand.

'Hallo, Mrs. Day! Had your tea?'

'No, not yet,' said Irene.

'Oh! I'll tell Cook. She is here, I suppose?'

'Yes, she's just gone into the kitchen. We're ready for breakfast now.'

'Oh, breakfast! I forgot that. Me and the guv always have ours before we go to bed, and then just a cuppa in the morning. The waitress will be here in a minute. I'll tell her to lay it in the lounge.' Mrs. Handen put her cup and saucer on a table, and went to interview the cook.

Mr. Handen wandered into the saloon with a cup of tea in his hand.

'Oh, hallo! Morning, Mrs. Dray.'

'Good morning, Mr. Handen. Lovely day, isn't it?'

'Yes, filthy. Where is everybody?'

'Mrs. Handen is in the kitchen.'

'Where are the cleaners? Ain't they come yet?'

'Good morning, guv!' came a cheery voice from the floor of the private bar.

'Good morning, guv,' came another cheery voice, from the floor of the public bar.

'Oh, there you are! Where's your husband, Mrs. Ray?'

'Down in the cellar.'

'Oh.' Mr. Handen put his cup on the counter with a shaky hand. 'Filthy stuff! Bloomin' housemaid can't make tea. Tastes like ruddy ditchwater. Enough to drive a man to drink.' He went to the spirit locker and poured himself a third of a tumbler of gin, and splashed into it the same amount of tonic water. 'Ah !' he said a moment later. 'That's better !' He emptied the glass, and mixed another drink similar to the first one, and swallowed that. 'Filthy tonic water they make nowadays, worse than the ginger ale.' He lit a cigarette, and meandering into the private bar, peered down through the hatchway into the cellar. 'Good morning, Mr. Hay !'

'Good morning, guv !'

He toddled back to the saloon, and the gin beginning to take effect, smiled at Irene.

'How-are-you-getting-on-all-right ?' he asked all in one word.

'Yes, thank you,' said Irene.

'That's the style ! Cor ! I got a filthy head on me this morning. Must be the tonic water. I'll have to cut it out.' He wandered upstairs to do his accounts.

Presently the waitress arrived and gave Irene and me our breakfast. Then three barmaids came in, and the potman ; and preparations for the day's business began in earnest. At a quarter to eleven I went down into the cellar and turned the beer on, and Mr. Handen tested the pumps and drank half a glass of bitter in each bar. By that time the guv was in quite a good mood, whistling cheerfully, and smiling at everyone ; and Mrs. Handen had her first Guinness of the day. The two cleaners changed and went home. The barmaids flocked into the kitchen to titivate. Alf the potman removed the last two crates of empties ; and Mrs. Handen had her

second Guinness of the day, and smiled for the first time.
At three minutes to eleven Alf ordered his breakfast; at
eleven o'clock he finished it and wiped his mouth with the
back of his hand; and he and Mr. Handen opened the house.

The old woman who had been the first customer the previous evening tottered in utter-
ing her parrot cry.

'Oh dear! first again. I
don't know what you'll think
of me. Guinness, dear, please.'

Mrs. Handen served her,
and, as usual, took two empty
bottles from the shopping
basket and exchanged them
for full ones without being
asked. Then several customers
came in, and presently Irene
noticed an insignificant little
man with watery eyes, who
seemed vaguely familiar to
her, staring over her shoulder
at nothing in particular.

'Half o' bitter, please,' he
said in a colourless voice without meeting her eyes.

*An insignificant little man
with watery eyes*

Mr. Handen slipped casually, but quickly, into the private
bar where I was serving.

'Here, Mr. Ray, come here,' he said, drawing me to a
place where we could see a part of the saloon mirrored in a
glass panel of a door. 'See that little twerp your wife is
serving?'

'Yes,' I said.

'Know him?'

'Er—don't think so; I'm not sure. He looks familiar. Why? Who is he?'

' "Grimes" is his name. "Slimy Grimes" we call him. Get an eyeful of him while he can't see you; he's one of the firm's spies.'

'Spies! What's the firm want spies for?'

'Why, to spy on the likes o' you and me, of course, and count the number o' drinks we have, and tell the directors every time we open half a minute late, or slip across the road to buy ourselves a pair o' socks during open hours. That's what they're for. You want to watch them swine. You can't laugh too hearty at a smutty joke with one o' them in the house, or they go and tell the directors you was drunk. Ain't you been told about them?'

'No, it's a new one on me.'

'Huh! That's the first thing a learner wants to learn.'

'But—er—is it a regular thing, having spies?'

'In this line? You bet! Most of the big firms have them. But you soon get to know 'em. I can spot 'em the first time they come in. There's two comes to this house. We call the other one "Mephi" because he's got eyebrows like a imitation Satan. He brings a woman with him sometimes as a sort o' cover. Put your missis on to Slimy when you get the chance; I'm going up to the office to phone the firm's houses on either side and let 'em know he's in the district. Tell your missis not to be short with him, or anything, or you'll both be for it. They're dangerous, them blighters. It's best to treat 'em kind, however much you hate 'em.'

'I get you. Thanks for telling me.'

'That's all ri——' Mr. Handen stopped in the middle of a word, and glared into the saloon. 'Hell! we're getting 'em

all here this morning. See that fat bloke what's coming in?
He's another one you got to watch. Can't stop now; got to
phone the other houses. Go and lush him up; he's important. I'll tell you about him afterwards.' He hurried through
the lounge to the stairs, smiling at the fat man on the way.
'Morning, Mr. Green. Can't stop now; got a phone call.
See you presently.'

I heard the name, but it meant nothing to me.

'All right, Mr. Handen,' smiled Mr. Green. 'All right, all
right.' He waggled his umbrella, and made for the counter.

He was a short fat man with a jovial manner, about sixty
years old. At first sight I thought he didn't look a bad sort of
chap; except for his eyes. I didn't like those; they were small
and piggy, and too close together. As he hung his umbrella
on the counter he shot birdlike glances to each side, rather
in the manner of a fat sparrow approaching a piece of cake
in the park. Then he looked at me and smiled. He had quite
a nice smile. I began to like him again.

'Good morning, Mr. Day,' he said. 'How are you?'

'Oh, you know me!'

'Yes. Don't you know me?'

'No,' I said tactlessly.

'Oh!' He looked quite surprised at that; and then
blushed as if annoyed as well. 'I thought you'd know me by
now. Give me a drop o' Scotch, will you?'

I poured him a single and put it beside a water carafe.

'Er—double,' he smiled.

I added another single

'Put a drop o' water in it, will you?'

Wondering why a man couldn't water his own whisky
when there was a carafe at his elbow, I splashed in some
eight drops or so.

'Phew! Careful! Don't drown it,' he cried.

Then I saw why he couldn't add the water himself. His hand shook so badly when he picked up the glass that he could only just raise it to his lips. He emptied it in two noisy gulps and returned it clumsily to the counter.

'Similar.'

I gave him another double, and this time, to be on the safe side, added only seven drops of water.

'Mild-and-bitter, please,' said a customer.

'Shan't be a minute,' I replied, waiting to be paid for the two double whiskies.

'Never mind me,' smiled Mr. Green. 'Attend to the customers; I'm in no hurry.'

Wondering who the heck this Mr. Green could be, I served the mild-and-bitter; and then for the next few minutes was kept busy with other customers.

Meanwhile Mr. Handen came back from the telephone.

'Have a drink?' said Mr. Green, raising the flap for him.

'Thank you, I'll have a bitter,' muttered Mr. Handen with a covert glance in my direction, which was entirely mis-interpreted.

I could see he was fuming inwardly, but failed to spot the reason. I thought it was merely because he disliked Mr. Green; but it was only partly that. He wanted some gin. I had not realized at that time that no intelligent publican would ever let his firm know he drank spirits. No intelligent publican ever does drink spirits, of course, but that is another matter. Nor did it occur to me just then that all publicans—intelligent or otherwise—dislike intensely to swop drinks with a man who favours double whiskies against their own half-pints of beer, which was the main, though not the whole, crux of this situation.

'Same again for you?' inquired Mr. Handen enviously, as he went behind the counter.

'Yes, please,' smiled Mr. Green, carefully counting out the exact price of one double whisky. Then very pointedly he put beside it the exact amount due for half a pint of bitter at the public-bar price—spirits were the same in all bars—and then saw me looking at him. 'Oh!' he exclaimed in a loud voice. 'Er—I'd better settle for what I had when you were upstairs.' He added some more money.

I noticed he added only enough for one double whisky, and was on the point of reminding him he'd had two double whiskies while Mr. Handen was upstairs, but an inner voice warned me against it. So, instead, I decided to amuse myself by watching the by-play; and presently observed him fiddling with an empty glass.

'Have another?' murmured Mr. Handen politely, but not pressingly.

'Don't mind if I do.'

'Single?' inquired Mr. Handen hopefully.

'Double,' said Mr. Green firmly.

Mr. Handen gave some money to the barmaid.

'Ring up a double whisky and a bitter, Kath,' he mumbled. 'Er—public-bar price for the bitter,' he added disgustedly; and pouring out the drinks, he dribbled six drops of water into Mr. Green's glass, and raised his own. 'Cheerio!'

'Chin-chin,' said Mr. Green. 'Where's Mrs. Day?'

'In the kitchen, I expect.'

'Oh, good! I'm supposed to be inspecting you today. The directors are going to some meeting or other. The cellar's all right, eh? Everything—er—— ?'

'Yes, it's still there,' grinned Mr. Handen who knew how frightened Mr. Green was of the rickety ladder.

Mr. Green smiled gratefully at the news.

'Returns all up to date?'

'Yes,' replied Mr. Handen, grinning broadly because he knew how Mr. Green hated climbing stairs.

'Oh, fine! Well, there's no need to bother with the kitchen if Mrs. Day's there. I'll have another before I go. Er—by the way, I forgot my wallet this morning. Left it in my other coat; and it's too late to get to the bank now. You couldn't —er—be my banker today, could you, old boy?'

'Certainly,' said Mr. Handen, trying not to groan, as he reached for the spirit measure. 'How much d'you want?'

'Well—er—a couple o' quid would be handy.'

Mr. Handen plopped a double whisky into Mr. Green's glass, and then peered dubiously into the depths of his wallet, as if surprised by its lack of co-operation.

'Er—how much did you say?'

'A pound will see me through if you're short, old boy.'

Mr. Handen laid a note on the counter.

'Shall I take for the whisky?'

'Suppose so. You don't want another, do you?'

'No, thank you,' muttered Mr. Handen, picking the note up again, and putting it in the glass by the till.

Mr. Green swallowed the whisky neat, accepted the change, and turned to go.

'I must be off now. I'll let 'em know at Head Office that the cellar and the returns are all right. Thanks for the er ... er. Goo'-bye.'

'Bye-bye,' grunted Mr. Handen.

Mr. Green went out smiling, to pay his next business call.

Mr. Handen turned to me.

'See all that? That's the sort o' thing you got to put up with when you're only a manager.'

'Who is he?' I asked.

'Gawd knows. Sort o' permanent orderly sergeant and general toady to the directors; and mark my words, every blessed thing you say to him goes back to 'em. In fact, if you actually want anything to get to Head Office without having to tell them yourself, just tell him and they'll know all about it the same day. Did you see him borrow a quid off me?'

'Yes. Rather neatly done, I thought.'

'You've said it; and he'll borrow another in about three weeks' time; and a month later he'll give it back to me and swear blind he returned the first one the week after he had it. He works that one on you about three times a year. Four, if you don't watch out. Cor! he's red hot; and so damned civil with it too! But if you kick up a row you're for it; he'll get you somehow. They always believe him before you, you know.'

'But surely you can do something about it!'

'Some has tried, but they ain't lasted long. Managing director's fancy boy, that's what he is; knows where the body's hid, I reckon. Where's Slimy Grimes? He gone?'

'Yes; he went directly Mr. Green came in.'

'Ha! That's what they do when they meet. One goes out; and you didn't see 'em recognize each other, did you?'

'No—can't say I did.'

'Rummy, ain't it? I suppose they think we're dumb. Well, p'r'aps we are. By the way, tell your missus she can come out o' the kitchen now if that's where she is; there won't be no directors here this morning.' Mr. Handen grinned and poured himself a double gin. 'Might as well have one on the house, seeing I'm a quid down. How many whiskies did he have while I was phoning?'

'Two doubles.'

'Hm . . . and only paid me for one . . . and I bought him one. He's two doubles up—less half a pint o' bitter at the public-bar price—and my quid into the bargain. Bloomin' wonder, ain't he? Still, it might have been worse. I'll get it back somehow; and if the firm catches me I'll get the sack for fiddling, and no reference. Well, here's to a good tenancy. Cheerio!'

XIX

THE next day summer came suddenly to London. Bright
sunshine poured from a cloudless sky; and the newspapers
said we were in for a long hot spell. Striped curtains were
dragged from the back of the linen cupboard and draped in
the doorways; ice buckets were filled with lager beer; and
everyone grumbled incontinently at the heat and the English
climate, especially Mr. Handen whose idea of combating the
high temperature was to change from occasional gins with
a little bitter to numerous lagers with lots of gin.

'What you ought to do,' I told him, 'is to take a day off
to get yourself used to the change. Pack a couple o' quarts
of lager and some sandwiches, and take Mrs. Handen to
Kew Gardens and find a nice shady tree by the lake. It
would do you both a world of good.'

'Suit me,' he said; 'but there ain't no relief couples to
spare. Too many managers on their summer holidays.'

'What about we two?'

'Cor! that's an idea. I'll go and ring up Head Office.' He
went at once, and five minutes later was back behind the
counter. 'It's okay. We got Monday off. They seem to think
a lot of you two up there.'

'Oh, do they? Good!'

On Monday I rose early so as to get the cellar done, and
also to make a list of everything that would be required for
the day before the Handens were ready to go. Happening to
pass the kitchen door, I saw Mrs. Handen, in nightdress and
bedroom slippers, putting a kettle on the stove. Presently I
heard her calling the cleaners.

'Pat! Sue!'

Pat looked up from her pail.

'Yes, madam?'

'Have the papers come?'

'Yes, I'll bring 'em.' Pat dropped her scrubbing-brush, fetched the newspapers from the mat, and bounced along to the kitchen like a good-natured rubber ball. 'Morning, madam.'

'Good morning, Pat. No letters?'

'Postman ain't been yet. Up early ain't yer? Having a day off?'

'Yes.'

'All right, I'll bring yer tea up. You don't want to 'ang around 'ere in yer nightie; dustman'll be along presently.'

'Thanks, Pat. Is the water hot?'

'Fair.'

'Oh.'

'Be all right by the time you've 'ad yer tea. You ought've told me yesterday.'

Mrs. Handen went upstairs; and as I passed the kitchen again I saw Pat adding enough water to the kettle to make tea for herself and Sue.

'Make enough for us, will you, Pat?'

'Course. What d'yer think?'

I liked Pat and Sue; they were always so cheerful. They were lifelong friends and very much alike, and both of them married and about thirty years old, and exactly the same height; but whereas Pat was short, chubby and perky, Sue was short, thin and perky.

At nine o'clock the cook and the kitchen maid came in, followed by the housemaid an hour late, because she knew her mistress was going out for the day and would be getting up early to make her own tea and so wouldn't miss her. By then the house was fairly awake. Later on, when Irene and I were at breakfast, Mr. Handen came wandering through the lounge on his way to the saloon, with a cup of cold tea in his hand. He always let his tea get cold before he drank it.

'Goo' morning, Mrs. Dray. Oh!—they called you *Day* at Head Office when I phoned 'em, didn't they? Sorry. Good morning, Mr. Day. Where's everybody? Ain't the cleaners come yet?'

'Drunk yer tea, guv?' shouted Pat from the private bar.

'Oh! of course, I've seen her before; she brought the tray up. Morning, Pat and Sue, wherever you are.' He put his cup on the counter with a shaking hand. 'Filthy stuff! Ruddy housemaid can't make tea. Stuff'd drive a man to drink.' He helped himself to three fingers of gin and a baby tonic water.

Irene and I, who were watching this morning routine from our breakfast table just inside the lounge, chuckled quietly to ourselves.

'When are you off, guv?' I asked.

'As soon as the old lady's got herself up. It always takes her half the day when she's going out.' He looked at himself in an advertisement mirror, said 'Blimey, what a tie!' and went upstairs to change it.

A little while after I had opened the house Mrs. Handen sailed into the saloon, resplendent in her outdoor apparel: a gay hat in navy-blue with white trimmings, a silver fox stole (draped over one shoulder in deference to the sweltering summer day) and a black-and-white flowered frock. Dove-coloured gloves, a brown bag, nylon stockings and very tight high-heeled black shoes completed the ensemble. Pausing in front of a mirror advertising a proprietary whisky, she peered alternately first over one shoulder and then over the other, trying to check the hang of her skirt at the back, but finding it too much of a struggle, gave up and glanced at the clock.

'Goodness! Look at the time; and I haven't had my elevenses yet.'

Irene dutifully reached for a bottle of stout.

'Not a Guinness, dear!' cried Mrs. Handen raising a hand. 'I'd never last the bus ride. Give me something short—a nice double gin.'

Irene gave her one.

'A tiny drop of water, as it's for yourself?' she suggested.

'Thanks, dear,' smiled Mrs. Handen, winking to show her appreciation of the subtle reference to her gins under the counter.

'Pay when you get back?' Irene asked facetiously.

Mrs. Handen nodded and drained her glass; and a man standing next to her—and thinking himself safe, no doubt, as she was just going out—smiled and asked:

'Going to have one with me, Mrs. Handen?'

'Thanks,' she said, to his disgust. 'Same again, Mrs. D. My boy friend's paying.'

'Come on, Maggie,' cried Mr. Handen from the other end of the bar.

'Oh, hallo, Harold! Didn't know you was down.' She swallowed the gift gin, and joined him. 'Ta-ta for now, Mrs. D. See you about closing time. Good-bye, all. Got the bag, Harold?'

'Course. S'long, everybody!'

Irene and I followed them to the door and watched them waddle along to the bus stop like a couple of faithful old ducks, Mrs. Handen limping a little, with ankles already swollen over the tops of her tight shoes, and the guv tugging irritably at the stiff white collar that he always insisted on wearing on his days out.

On our way back to the counter I glanced at the clock.

'Good lord!' I exclaimed. 'Do they call this a day off? It's nearly half past eleven already.'

'That's nothing,' laughed Kate. 'When relief couples come they don't get away till two sometimes. They're awful, some o' them relief couples, asking questions all the time.'

'They could have gone before breakfast, as far as I was concerned,' I said. 'Oh, well, I hope they enjoy themselves.' I grinned at Irene.

She grinned back. We guessed what would happen. They would take the Underground from the West End, go to the first pub at Kew and stay there till closing time, then waddle into the gardens and tuck into the sandwiches and lager under the first tree, and sleep till opening time came round again. Then they would return to the pub, and eventually arrive home full of gin and good humour at about midnight.

As far as the first part of the programme was concerned we were not far wrong. When closing time came they had not arrived; so I locked and bolted the house, and the two of us cashed up for them. After several re-counts, it being the first occasion on which we had been through the whole process by ourselves, we came to the reluctant conclusion that one of the tills was a shilling and a penny short, one of them a penny up and the other fourpence up.

That worried us quite a lot, because we thought (quite rightly, of course) that the cash should always accord with the till readings; and it was not until we had turned back a few pages of the till book that we discovered how rarely it did, and that our re-counts were so much wasted effort.

'Well, I'm blowed!' I cried. 'It's hardly ever dead right! Why! this isn't so bad, is it? Especially for our first day.'

'Pretty hot stuff, if you ask me,' beamed Irene. 'We're only eightpence out altogether. I bet old Fatty Grainger would be green with envy. I vote we have a drink on this.'

'You bet!' said I. 'We won't waste a second. I reckon we've earnt one on the house too.'

'Oh, yes,' said Irene judicially; 'because we're a relieving couple today. I bet all reliefs have one or two; it's only natural. I'll pour out while you do the till book.'

As she reached for the glasses we heard the telephone bell.

'I'll go,' I said, and ran up to the office. 'Hallo?'

'That you, Mr. Day?'

'Speaking.'

'Mr. Marnes here.'

'Oh, good evening, sir!'

'Good evening, Mr. Day. I've just had some bad news about Mr. and Mrs. Handen. They've had an accident. Been knocked down by a lorry, and they're both in hospital.'

'Oh, lord! Badly hurt?'

'Yes; I'm afraid it'll be a long job. Mrs. Handen's broken an arm and two ribs, and he's broken a leg and cut his head badly.'

'Phew! How did it happen?'

'Oh—er—as far as I can make out, he dropped a bag he was carrying, and they both made a grab at it and fell over in front of the lorry.'

'I say! That's terrible, isn't it!'

'Yes-yes—quite—of course it is; but what about the business? That's what I want to know. Can you carry on for a while? I mean, we're short of relief couples just now, with so many managers on holiday.'

'Oh, I shall be all right, sir. Don't you worry.'

'But I am worrying. Are you sure? Because it won't do you any good if—er—I mean, it would be far better for you if you're not quite confident, to say so now.'

'I'm absolutely confident, sir.'

'All right, then. I'll send Mr. Green along for a few days to keep an eye on things.'

That didn't sound too good to me.

'Eh!—d'you mean to live here?' I exclaimed, thinking of the whisky stocks.

'No-no, just to visit you each day till you get the hang of things.'

I thought I heard him chuckle when he said that. I suppose he thought I had sensed a reflection on my ability to run the house.

'By the way,' he continued, 'you'll have to have the stocks taken. The man will probably come tomorrow afternoon. Get everything ready for him, as far as you can, will you?'

'Yes, sir.'

'Right you are, then, Mr. Day. Phone me if there's anything you're not sure about. And don't forget to bank the takings in the morning; and—er—watch your stocks, won't you?'

'Right you are, sir.'

'Good night.'

'Good night, sir.'

I put the receiver back and lit a cigarette, and walked thoughtfully out of the office, and across the landing, and started slowly downstairs, worrying about the poor old Handens. Then the full significance of the news striking me,

I broke into a run, jumped the last few stairs, and rushed through the lounge into the saloon.

'I say, buddy!'

Irene swung round, startled by my tone.

'What's up!'

'Sweetheart! Marvellous news! We're in charge of the pub!'

'What!'

I told her what had happened.

'Oh, the poor darlings! What a shame! But, Bill—Bill! We're *managers*! We're PUBLICANS!'

'Terrific, isn't it!' I lapsed into silence, my brain cloyed with happiness; and noticing the drinks Irene had mixed while I was upstairs, I picked one of them up and absent-mindedly swallowed it at a draught, hardly knowing what I was doing. It just seemed a natural action. 'We must have a drink on this, sweetheart,' I cried as soon as I was capable of speech again.

'Definitely!' she agreed. 'Oh, darling, you've drunk yours!'

'Have I! I didn't notice. Never mind, I'll have another. What about you?' I snatched a bottle of gin. 'Oh, you've still got one!'

'Yes; but—Bill! *Bill!*' She was frowning at me.

'What's up!'

She frowned at the bottle in my hand.

'Darling—*what about our stocks?*'

'Oh!' I hadn't thought about that. Of course—our stocks! Hmm . . .? Then it occurred to me. 'Don't be silly,' I said, 'they haven't been checked yet.'

'Oh, no, of course not! Well, all right, you mix them. I'll drink this one quickly. Chin-chin!'

'Honky-tonk!' I poured two more. 'Sad about the Handens, isn't it?'

'Mm, isn't it? Hope they get better. Is this mine?'

'Yep. Here's to us!' I flung an arm round her waist.

'Look out!' she laughed; 'you're spilling it.'

'Well, drink it, you ass!' I cried.

She gulped it excitedly, and laughed again.

'Oh, isn't life wonderful!'

'You bet!' I laughed. 'And only eightpence down on the day! Come on, let's get this cash put away; we shall have to be up early tomorrow.'

XX

DIRECTLY we were dressed the next morning I hurried downstairs to do my cellar work, so as to leave plenty of time for easing myself into my managerial duties. Irene stayed in the bedroom and made up the three till floats; because, as the key of the safe was in Mr. Handen's trouser pocket, we had taken the cash upstairs, in the till drawers, and hidden it in our wardrobe for the night.

On my way through the lounge I told Pat about the accident. The news didn't seem to sink in at first. Then presently, she looked up from her pail.

'Who's in charge of the 'ouse?'

'I am,' I grinned.

'Coo!' she cried, and jumped up and ran into the public bar.

'Sue! we got a new guv. Mr. and Mrs. 'Anden are in 'ospital.'

I left them chattering together, and went into the cellar. When I came up again I found the potman leaning against the saloon counter staring thoughtfully into space.

'Good morning, Alf,' I said.

'Is it right as 'ow the guv and his missis is in 'orspital?' he asked without returning my salutation.

'Yes.'

'Mmm! Head Office sending someone down to take over the 'ouse?'

'No. I'm in charge.'

'Oh!' Alf didn't seem to like that. Not that it could

matter to him who was in charge; but he had been working
for nearly twenty years in public houses; and he was still a
potman. He looked me up and down, as if to say: 'What do
you know about running a pub? You only been in the line
five minutes.' It was easy to read his thoughts. Class dis-
tinction, that's what it was. He decided to go all working
class with himself. 'Ho! So you're in charge, are you? Well,
what bottles d'you want up this morning?'

'Same as usual.'

'Four cases o' light and a couple o' browns in 'ere?'

'Yes—if that's what's needed.'

'I'm asking *you*, mister.'

'Why ask me?' I grinned. 'You've been here long enough,
haven't you? Can't you tell what's wanted by looking at the
shelves?'

'It ain't my place to decide if you're in charge.'

'Does Mr. Handen always tell you what to put up?'

'Course he don't; he leaves it to me.'

'Well, that's what I'm doing.'

'Yus, but I don't know your ways.'

'I haven't any ways yet,' I said, and sighing, walked through
the bars and made a pencilled list of what was required.
'There you are. Put that lot up.'

'Thank yer. Got enough Guinnesses down, ain't yer, for a
Tuesday?'

'Never mind.'

'Mm! Mr. 'Anden wouldn't 'ave all them Worthingtons
up neither. It ain't Saturday.'

'Oh, get on with your work, man.'

'I ain't used to being spoke to like that.'

I ignored that, and went to fetch the cigarettes and
tobacco, which had been hidden in the bedroom with the

cash. Passing the kitchen, I heard the cook's voice raised in shrewish tones.

'Oh, indeed ! And so she's in charge, is she ! Well, I never !'

It seemed the cook was going all working class, too ! I paused to listen.

'Martha, run up to Mrs. Day and ask her 'ow she wants the meat cooked.'

'Oh, Cook, you know you never ask Madam 'ow she wants it done !'

'Go on, I'm waiting.'

'Oh, Cook !'

'Go on !'

I ran upstairs, and was just coming out of the bedroom with the tobacco and cigarettes when Martha came plodding up. She stood politely aside for me to pass out, and then knocked on the door; and the following conversation ensued.

'Cook's compliments and 'ow d'you want the meat done ?' gabbled Martha.

'Eh ?' muttered Irene spreading a fistful of florins on the back of a suitcase. 'What kind of meat is it ?'

'Dunno, I ain't seen it.'

'Two four six eight ten—one pound. Well then, how the heck should I know how to cook it ?'

'Dunno. What shall I tell her ?'

'Twelve fourteen sixteen eighteen twenty—two pounds. Tell her what I said. One two three four five six . . .'

Martha stumped crossly downstairs; but a few minutes later she was standing in the doorway again.

'Cook says the butcher says as 'ow it's roasting meat, but it ain't 'ardly worth stewing.'

'All right. That's twelve pounds in that till.'

'What shall I tell 'er?'

'Oh, tell her what you like. Can't she make it into sausages or something? I'm busy. Floats—twelve, twelve, twelve—thirty-six pounds.'

Martha clumped downstairs again, and I was just in time to overhear the following.

'She says as 'ow you're to do as you think best, and if you think I'm climbing all them stairs again, I ain't. You can go yourself.'

'That'll do, Martha!'

'Well, I ain't; and she says as 'ow you can make it into sausages if you like.'

Then there was a girlish titter from the direction of the sink, followed by the sound of potatoes tumbling into a bowl. A moment later Irene came downstairs with the drawer of the saloon till. While she was pushing it into place the cook came in.

'Good morning, Mrs. Day.'

'Good morning, Cook.'

'The greengrocer's here. How much cabbage d'you want me to order?'

'How much do we need?'

'Well, it depends, don't it?'

'Oh dear!' Irene looked into the public bar, where I was arranging packets of shag on the shelves. 'I've put twelve pounds in each till. That all right?'

'Yes, thanks, dear. Make a note on the pad.'

She turned back to the cook.

'Oh, you still here! Don't you know how much to order?'

'Well, it's up to you if you're in charge, ain't it, Mrs. Day?'

Irene sighed.

'I suppose so; but I've a lot to do. Send the greengrocer to me.'

'Very well, Mrs. Day.' Cook flounced back to the kitchen.

Presently the greengrocer came in.

'Good morning, madam. How much cabbage would you like? Same as usual?'

'Yes, please.'

'Very good, madam. Sorry to trouble you.'

Irene went upstairs for another till drawer; and a barmaid called Pat arrived, and smiled at Pat the cleaner.

'Good morning, Pat,' said Pat the cleaner. 'Guv and Madam are in 'ospital with multiple injuries and Mr. Day's in charge.'

'No! Go on, Pat!'

'They are, Pat. They've 'ad a naccident.'

'Oh lor!'

The waitress came in.

'Good morning, Pat.'

'Morning, Nora,' smiled Pat the cleaner. 'Guv and Madam are in 'ospital with multiple injuries and Mr. Day's in charge.'

A messenger arrived with Mr. Handen's keys, and said that the guv was too bad to see anyone; and admitted, on being questioned, that he had not asked after Mrs. Handen.

'Cor! Call yerself a man!' shouted Sue from the public bar.

The other two barmaids came in.

'Hallo, you ladies of leisure, you're late,' grinned Pat the cleaner. 'You won't half cop it; we've got a new guv. Mr. and Mrs. 'Anden are in 'ospital with multiple injuries and Mr. Day's in charge.'

'What's that, Pat?'

'Multiple injuries, and Mr. Day's in charge.'

'Gertcha!'

'S'true. Ask Pat; she's in the kitchen.'

The draught beer arrived, and as Alf was in the bottled-beer store sulking, I had to go into the cellar and see it in. I also had to make out the order for the next delivery; but with only the vaguest idea of the average consumption of the house, that was something of a problem; so I ran up to the office, found the corresponding order for the previous week, and copied that. Then, while giving the draymen their customary pints of mild ale in the public bar I noticed there were only three bottles of lemonade on the shelves. At that moment Alf appeared, and asked if he should see the draught beer in.

'It's in,' I snapped; 'and by the way, this bar is short of lemonades.'

'You never put none on yer list,' he growled.

'Good heavens, man, couldn't you see there were only three bottles left? Bring two cases, and then go down and tidy the cellar.'

'It ain't my job to . . .'

But I didn't stay to hear what his job wasn't. I had just remembered that yesterday's takings had to be banked; and running up to the office again, I grabbed some money-bags and took them to the bedroom. Irene came in for the third till drawer just as I finished counting the notes.

'How are you getting on, cocky?'

'Not too bad,' I grinned. 'Fizz down to the office and see if you can find a paying-in book, will you?'

'Righto. What's it look like?'

'Oh, heck! don't you know? Well, never mind, I'll go.'

When I came back from the bank the bottled beer was

arriving, and as Alf was now sulking in the mineral-water store I had to see it in myself. While giving the draymen their customary pints of mild ale it occurred to me that I hadn't the foggiest notion how much bottled beer the house used in a week, so I copied the delivery note on to the order form and gave them that. There was no time for fancy calculations, and anyway, bottled beer didn't go bad if kept too long, like the draught stuff did, so what the heck! I had just added my signature when Irene came in.

'Oh, darling, have you a moment to spare?'

'Yes, my beautiful,' I grinned, sensing trouble. 'What's up?'

'I forgot to tell you there's only two and thruppence worth of coppers for the three tills, and we're frightfully short of sixpences and shillings.'

'Heck! Where's Alf?'

'I haven't seen him for ages. Isn't he getting some lemonade up?'

'Oh, never mind then, I'll go.' I dashed up to the bedroom and grabbed a handful of notes, ran to the bank, and rushed back just in time to see the mineral waters arrive; and as Alf was sulking in the cellar by then, I had to check them in myself. I had no idea, of course, what to order for next week; but still, it only took a few moments to copy the delivery note on to the order form. Just as I was signing that Irene looked in to say the local food office had been on the phone.

'Oh?' I said. 'What did they want?'

'Wanted to know when we were going to send in our E five-sixty-three A, or something, because it's a fortnight overdue. He seemed quite cross.'

'Oh, gosh! What did you say?'

'Well, I had to think quickly, so I said it was in the post and he should have had it by now. Then he got quite nice and said he was sorry he'd ter-roubled me.'

'Clever girl! What is it, anyway?'

'Haven't the foggiest.'

'Oh! Well, never mind, we'll find out somehow. You wrote that number down, of course? D, whatever it was. Eh?'

'Well—er—no, but I'm pretty certain it was nine-sixty-three, unless it was fifty-three, of course; but the first letter wasn't D, darling, it was E—or was it B! Anyway, it wasn't C. The only thing I'm not sure about is the A; but I shouldn't think that matters, right at the end, would you?'

'Oh, no! sweetheart. Merely a matter of form, I should say. Heaven help the clerks at the food office.'

'Why, darling, have I made a mess of it?'

'Lord, no! you've done magnificently. I must remember that answer: "It's in the post and you should have had it by now." The Prime Minister couldn't have made a better one to the Opposition. You did once tell me you had an ancestor in the Diplomatic Corps, didn't you?'

'Oh, shut up! Have we enough spirits out?'

'Heck! I'd forgotten them. Where are the governor's keys? Oh, I must have left them sticking in the safe. Here's the small silver for the tills; the pennies are on the counter. Whack it out equally between the three of them while I get the spirits, will you?'

'Righto.'

I dashed upstairs for the keys, and returning a few moments later, found Irene frowning at three heaps of sixpences.

'Sweety pie,' she said plaintively, 'how d'you divide five pounds' worth of sixpences equally between three tills?'

'You don't, my beautiful, you get it as near as you can, and then change the odd coins into pennies and divide those.'

'Oh, aren't you clever!'

'Not really,' I grinned. 'I learnt that from Fatty Grainger.'

'And do you do the same with the shillings?'

'I expect so,' I laughed, glancing at the clock. 'I say! we open in three minutes, and I haven't had my breakfast yet. Seen Alf lately?'

'No, but there's a light in the cellar.'

I ran to the hatch.

'Alf!'

'Yus?'

'Come on, man, it's nearly opening time.'

'All right, I can't do everything at——' he began. Then, apparently remembering his breakfast, he changed his tune. 'All right, Mr. Day,' he shouted cheerfully, 'just comin''; and scrambling up the ladder, he hurried into the saloon, muttered, 'Give us me pint, dear,' to the barmaid, grabbed the keys from the board, and went round to the front of the counter. Then he drank his breakfast in three gulps, and opened the house.

XXI

THE first person to come in was Mr. Green, who arrived watch in hand and very hot.

'Ah! good morning, Mr. Day. Glad to see you're open on time. Have Mr. Handen's keys come yet?'

'Yes, some time ago.'

'Ah, good! We'll get the takings to the bank presently, and then I'll run through the returns with you.'

'I've done that.'

'What? The returns?'

'No. Paid in yesterday's takings.'

'Oh, fine! Well, that gives us a breather; we can do the returns later. Terrible business this, about the Handens!'

'Frightfully bad luck, isn't it!'

'Yes. Upsetting. I think I'll have a drop o' Scotch.'

'Double?' I asked smiling.

'Yes, better make it a double.'

I poured it out and added six drops of water; and just then a barmaid looked in to say I was wanted in the private bar.

'All right, I'll settle for this later,' muttered Mr. Green hastily. 'Attend to your business.'

A hard-faced woman had come to clear a collecting box. With myself as witness, she abstracted four dusty pennies and a French ha'penny, and then re-sealed the box and wrote me a receipt for fourpence, and after refusing a drink as if I had insulted her, stalked out, saying over her shoulder that an official acknowledgement would be sent to me by post in due course.

'Oh, that's all right,' I said, blushing at the small amount, and not a little sorry for the orphans. 'Please don't bother; it's hardly worth the postage.'

For one fleeting moment I thought of calling her back and making a personal donation; until it occurred to me that there were several collecting boxes in each bar. Then to soothe my feelings I bought myself a Worthington, and had a long cosy chat with an old woman whose daughter suffered with floating kidneys. In the ordinary way I'm not frightfully fond of kidneys, floating or otherwise, but anything was better than nattering to Mr. Green—who just then happened to be watching Irene arranging the snacks on the glass shelves.

'Good morning, Mrs. Day,' he said when he saw she had not noticed him.

'Oh! Hallo, Mr. Green. Nice to see you again. Feeling fit?'

'Well, just a little puffed, you know, with the warm weather and running for the bus.'

'Double?' inquired Irene smiling.

'Yes, please, Mrs. Day.'

'Give Mr. Green a double whisky, Kath.'

Kath poured it out and added seven drops of water.

'Phew! Steady!' he muttered. 'Don't drown it.'

Irene went back to the kitchen for more snacks.

Mr. Green smiled at the hovering barmaid.

'That's all right, dear, I'll settle with Mr. Day presently.'

He emptied his glass just as I came back after finishing my Worthington.

'Being looked after, Mr. Green?'

'Well—er—I was just going to order a drop o' whisky.'

I poured him a double.

'Let me see, I owe you for one already, don't I?' he said,

counting out the price of two double whiskies, and happily ignoring the one served by Kath.

'Thank you,' said I unsuspectingly.

Kath, thinking he was paying for the drink she had supplied, smiled and went on with her work.

It will be realized, of course, that the above was all pieced together afterwards by Irene, Kath and myself.

As his hands were not shaking so much now as they were when he first came in he added the water himself this time. Presently he asked me if I knew the stocktaker was coming that afternoon.

'Yes,' I said; 'and that reminds me, I must run upstairs in a minute and get the returns done.'

'Know how to do them?'

'Oh, I'll soon find out.'

'I'll show you. That's one of the things I'm here for.' He emptied his glass, smiled, and thumped it on the counter. 'Come on.'

Followed by myself, he puffed slowly upstairs, tottered across the landing to the office, and eased himself into the chair at the desk and after rummaging in the drawers, found the necessary books and forms. Then, the climb up the stairs having set his hands shaking again, he scratched a somewhat spidery date on the first form.

'Heart's bad this morning,' he puffed. 'I wonder if—er— a little something just to—er—you know . . .?'

'Drop o' whisky?'

'Well—erm—it might be a good idea. Don't do this generally, of course.'

'Righto, I'll run down and get it.'

'Better bring one for yourself while you're at it,' he smiled. 'Might as well be sociable while we're working.'

'Oh, thanks very much,' said I, beaming at this pleasant gesture.

But apparently it was not an invitation, after all, for he glanced hastily out of the window, and frowned darkly. At the bottom of the stairs I was met by Irene.

'There's a man from the brewery to see Mr. Handen,' she said.

'Okay, I'll see him. Will you take Mr. Green a drink? He's dying of heart disease.'

'Righto.'

The man from the brewery introduced himself to me as Mr. Muir. He was a little, wizened, beery-faced man dressed like an undertaker, and wore old-fashioned spectacles with metal frames. He seemed very short-sighted.

'I'm the cellar-inspector,' he said. At least, that was obviously his meaning. What he actually said was 'I'm a shellar inshpector.' Apparently he had already inspected a cellar that morning.

'I see,' I said. 'Coming down?'

'Yesh,' he lisped. 'Bring a couple o' glashes, will you?'

'Okay,' I smiled.

He lurched cheerfully round the cellar, leering myopically at the stencilled numbers on the casks and noting them in a pocket book, and occasionally rapping a cask with his knuckles to gauge its contents. Then he took samples from two kilderkins of bitter beer that had been tapped ready for use, and went round the cellar again and measured every tapped cask properly with a dipstick, explaining to me at the same time the importance of using the beer in the order in which it arrived. Apparently that was 'mosh' important. Then he drank the two samples he had taken, and took two more, and gave me a lecture on beer-keeping, all of which I had heard several times before, in bits and pieces from Mr. Lawson, and at length from Mr. Handen, and at various times from all of the directors. By then the second two samples were ready for testing, and having rolled them professionally round and round his tongue and swallowed them with loud smacking noises, he congratulated me enthusiastically on the condition of the cellar and led the way up to the ground floor.

'Now I tesh all er beer thash connected up,' he lisped, and asked for a quarter of a pint to be drawn for him from each pump. These samples were held to the light, and smelt and tasted; and as he finished in each bar, the remains left in the glasses were mixed together in a pint mug and not wasted by Mr. Muir.

An envious customer in the public bar, unable to contain himself, burst out:

'Blimey! governor, 'ow much do they pay you for that?'

But Mr. Muir from the brewery did not deign to joke with public-bar customers. He smiled in an aloof manner and continued with his arduous duty. Then finishing up in the saloon, he passed to the customers' side of the counter and smiled at me.

'And now we'll have a little drink, shall we?' he whispered insinuatingly.

'That would be nice,' I grinned, having till then held only a watching brief. 'What would you like?'

'Half a pint of bitter from the third pump from the far end,' said he, pointing.

I pulled it up.

'And what about you?' he inquired.

I pulled up another half pint with the same pump; and to

my surprise he paid. It will be appreciated that I was thinking of the stocks. However, presently he had one with me !
Then I remembered Mr. Green sitting alone in the office,
and glancing at the clock, saw I had been occupied with the
inspection for nearly an hour.

'I say !' I exclaimed, 'I've got a chap in the office. I'd
forgotten all about him.'

'All right,' smiled Mr. Muir, 'I'll buzz off. Got another
couple o' cellars to do this morning.' He shook hands and
departed.

I hurried upstairs, worrying about the returns and Mr.
Green, but particularly about the returns, because I am not
much good at book work. On the plantation there had been
a competent *kanakapulle* (lit. child of accounts) to take care
of all the figures, and a still more competent European
accountant who called once a month to check them ; and
being far from a child of accounts myself, I was frightened
lest Mr. Green should be too offended by being kept waiting to initiate me properly.

I needn't have worried. He was fast asleep, with his
podgy fingers locked comfortably across his stomach.

'Ahem !' I coughed.

'Oh, there you are !' he grunted, reaching without thinking
for his empty glass. 'Pull up a chair.'

Luckily for me, P. H. Kent and Company's managers
were chosen for their administrative and social qualifications
rather than for any arithmetical talents they might possess,
and the books they were required to keep were designed
accordingly, so thirty minutes sufficed for Mr. Green to
teach me all I should know.

'And now we'll go downstairs and relax,' he murmured
when he had finished.

'Okay,' I smiled, much relieved at the easy turn of events. 'Thanks for explaining everything so clearly. Care for a drink?'

'Er—thanks, might as well.'

I followed him down to the saloon, and gratefully bought him a double whisky, and had a Worthington myself.

Later on he stood treat, but made the reasonable suggestion that as he was staying until the final closing time it would save trouble if he settled then for the whole day. I—having forgotten that I had missed my breakfast and was drinking on an empty stomach—amiably agreed, and presently switched from Worthingtons to pink gins, which he was soon calling 'gin pahits'; he having by then acquired a fair working knowledge of the Malay language; and I became convinced that if all the senior members of the firm were even half such good chaps as this bonny lad was I was going to have a whale of a time; and on advancing this opinion, was assured that it wasn't a bad firm, old boy, and given some useful hints on how to get in on it—such as, for example, that when officials from Head Office visited the house it wasn't a bad idea to extend to them a certain measure of hospitality. No need to overdo it, of course, my dear chap, but all the same it paid to be popular in the right quarter; and, after all, an efficient publican could always 'make up' the odd drink or two.

'Absolutely, old boy!' I beamed, being momentarily under the impression that the broad-minded gentleman was explaining that an occasional drink was conducive to efficiency. 'I'm completely with you. Definitely!'

Emboldened by my hearty agreement with his own sentiments, he then told me he would always help me with the firm in any way he could, and I said I would always help him in any way at all; which apparently, when I look back on the incident, was just what he hoped; because a little later on he suggested that I might be his banker that day, to which I replied that it would be an honour to do so to the extent of two pounds.

By that time I was in a completely carefree mood. Life, I felt, lay before me like a panorama of—well, of public houses, as it were. It was merely a matter of getting on. 'Jussa matter o' guts,' I explained to Mr. Green. 'That's all.' A slight tendency to lurch when I bent down, or turned too quickly, I naturally attributed to giddiness caused by over-work and missing my breakfast, and to the fact (hitherto unnoticed) that the space behind the counter was very cramped. Mr. Green was in an equally happy frame of mind, but otherwise—according to Irene—perfectly normal; though eventually we both missed our lunch.

A minute before closing time the stocktaker arrived; and a minute after closing time he started work. At some moment between the beginning and the end of those two minutes Mr. Green vanished from the house; apparently having decided to make a day of it. Nobody noticed him go, or minded that he had gone; least of all myself, who now had a new interest in life, and had forgotten all about the tally of his drinks. I was concerned solely with my stocks.

Luckily for me, in my inexperience, the stocktaker knew the house better than I did; so I merely trailed behind him, hoping for the best, and munching sandwiches pilfered from the snack cabinet, and unlocking cupboards and store-rooms, and watching dozens and dozens of bottles counted at a speed which made my head ache. The whole thing lasted about an hour and a quarter. Then he told me not to forget that my head office would require two sets of returns

for that day : one for the period before the stocks were taken,
and one for afterwards. Mr. Green had forgotten to mention
that ; and as I was somewhat dazed by the information, the
dear fellow kindly filled in the returns for the first half of
the day for me.

'You can copy these out in your own handwriting after
I've gone,' he grinned.

'Thanks most terrifically, old boy,' I murmured, amazed
not only by his thoughtfulness, but by his efficiency. I mean,
he worked so quickly. He was better than a *kanakapulle*.
And not nearly so condescending! 'Care for a drink, old
boy?' I beamed.

He said he was just ready for one; but hardly had we
blotted the returns than the telephone bell rang. It was the
firm's accountant, to know if I had checked the cash in the
safe.

'No; haven't had time yet. I've only just had my stocks
taken.'

'You should have done it before you opened.'

If that wasn't just like a head office! As bad as Brigade
H.Q. in the Army.

'Don't be an ass,' I said. 'I only got the ruddy key five
minutes before opening time.'

'Oh!—well, check it before you open this evening, will
you? I should have been along with one of the directors
to do it with you, but everything happened so suddenly.'

'All right, leave it to me.'

'Phone the result, will you?'

'Okay.' I slammed the receiver back and turned to the
stocktaker. 'Now I've got to check the ruddy cash,' I
growled. 'And I haven't had me perishing breakfast yet.'

'Come on, I'll help you, he grinned. 'Unlock the safe.'

He tumbled out the cash, and set to work with the speed and efficiency of a bookie's clerk. It hurt my eyes to watch him. In an amazingly short time he announced that the cash was four shillings and sixpence up.

'Good!' I cried. 'I'll phone and tell 'em it's dead right.'

'No, don't,' he said. 'Tell 'em it's four-and-six up; they'll think you're chiselling if you say it's dead right.'

'Oh!—oh, will they?' It was rather a shock to me to think anyone could imagine I chiselled—or whatever he called it. 'Okay then. I can do that later. What about that drink I promised you?'

'I wouldn't mind one of those Basses I've just been counting.'

We went down to the saloon, and I gave him one, but for myself prescribed a large gin with plenty of ginger ale. I was feeling tired and unappreciated by then. A certain reaction had set in since the morning session; and even a little thing like being told I should have checked the cash before opening had annoyed me. However, the gin soon confirmed me in my real opinion of myself: that I had the makings of a dashed fine publican.

'And now they're all yours,' remarked the stocktaker, putting down an empty glass.

'What are?' I asked.

'The stocks,' he grinned. 'This is where your troubles start.'

XXII

IRENE had been worrying about the form that was overdue at the food office, and while I was putting myself over with Mr. Green—or was it *vice versa*!—she had a brainwave. She would go to the hospital and ask Mrs. Handen about it. That would save mentioning it to Mr. Green or Head Office, and Mrs. Handen would not get into trouble for forgetting it. Also, she would be able to take both the Handens a little drop of something to cheer them up.

Irene visualized the Handens in crowded wards at opposite ends of the hospital, neither of the poor darlings having had a drink for twenty-four hours, and both of them with a hangover and in pain. So at closing time she took two bottles of gin up to their bedroom, and packed them in two suitcases together with night clothes, toilet requisites and other necessities, including the *Sporting Life Guide* and the *Licensed Victuallers' Gazette*, Mr. Handen's favourite mediums of literary relaxation, and a book entitled *Julie's Fate* that lay open by the bed which obviously belonged to Mrs. Handen. Then not being able to find me, because I'd disappeared somewhere with the stocktaker, she let herself out of the house without a word to anyone, and took a taxi to the hospital. There, of course, she had the usual trouble over calling at a non-visiting time—even after she had explained about the *D eight-fifty-nine K*, or whatever she was calling the thing by then—one foolish nurse even escorting her to a side door and directing her to the local food office. The only thing that saved her from a wasted afternoon was an unconscious way she has had ever since living in the East of treating all fools as refractory Tamil coolies; and as soon as she ceased to argue, her imperious manner carried her over all obstacles. In fact, her progress from the side door to Mrs. Handen's bed—after the foolish nurse accidentally gave away the number of the ward—was almost viceregal, the only check being when a pimply faced probationer clutched her by an arm and said with a smirk:

'Well, you can't see Mr. Handen, anyway, because he's got concussion, so there!'

'All right, child,' smiled Irene sweetly. 'Thank you for telling me,' and with that, she 'swep on', as the saying is.

She found Mrs. Handen, a frustrated mountain of pillows, plaster and bandages, looking very cross and sorry for herself; but her expression softened when she saw Irene strolling down the ward.

'Well now, fancy you coming to see me! None of me own people have been yet. Aren't we a couple of old fools!'

'Oh, we all have accidents,' smiled Irene comfortingly. 'Feeling pretty lousy?'

'Haven't half got a head on me,' moaned Mrs. Handen. 'Worse than me ribs and arm almost; but all they give me for it was a couple of aspirins. Don't seem to realize I'm a publican's wife. Couple o' double gins is what I want.'

'I've brought you some,' whispered Irene with a wary glance at the adjacent beds.

'What! Gin?'

'Yes; I've brought you a bottle.'

'Oh, dearie, you are a love! Give us a drop now. Don't let Sister see.'

There was a jug of water with a glass beside it on the pedestal by the bed, so with hands furtively below mattress level, Irene did the needful; and within five minutes Mrs. Handen was feeling considerably better.

'This is doing me good,' she smiled. 'I told Sister I could put up with the other pains if only she'd give me something to get rid of this head. "Give us a dollop o' brandy with the aspirins," I said, "and it'll work wonders." But would she take any notice! Lot o' teetotal spinsters they are here; they don't know what life is. I'd give something to see the old matron behind the public bar of a Saturday night. Wouldn't half wake her ideas up! Pour us another, dearie, will you? Then we'll put the bottle away till the night sister comes on. She's all right, I think.'

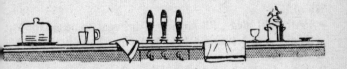

Irene surreptitiously did as she was asked, and presently mentioned the food form.

'Oh, that!' smiled Mrs. Handen. 'Has Cook forgotten it again? Remind her, dear. She always fills it up for me. I can't understand the thing. All about main meals and subsidiary whatnots. A meal is a meal to me. Governor can't understand it either. It's *Form E.G.C.*3, and it's called the Eight-Weekly. You'll find it in the waitress's drawer in the kitchen, where she keeps her plate powder and that.'

'Oh, thank you,' breathed Irene. 'I knew there was a three in it somewhere. So it goes in every eight weeks.'

'Every sixteen weeks. Used to be eight; that's why it's called the eight-weekly.'

'I see. By the way, I found some buff postcards from the Ministry of Food while I was looking for it. Anything to be done about those?'

'Yes. Chuck 'em in the dustbin, dear.'

'Oh! One came this morning about cooking fats . . .?'

'That's your grocer's job. Chuck it in the dustbin.'

'Oh! And there's one about meat.'

'That's the butcher's job. Chuck it in the dustbin, dearie. Chuck 'em all in the dustbin. You can't understand them; and even if you could the butcher and the grocer wouldn't agree with you; and you get hundreds of them during the year; and they get them too, so what's the odds! I say! this gin has took my head away; I believe I could get some sleep.'

'All right, dear, I'll go now. I brought some gin for Mr. Handen, but I suppose he'd better not have it if he's got concussion.'

'No, dear, chuck it in the—er—oh, wrap it up in me other nightie, and put it in the pedestal. Good night, dear, I'm off.'

Irene glanced at her watch. It was later than she thought, so after leaving Mr. Handen's things in the inquiries bureau she hurried to a telephone box and dialled the White Lark.

I had just said good-bye to the stocktaker when the bell rang; and I ran up to the office and grabbed the receiver.

'What cheer, cocky!' came her voice over the wire.

'Oh, hallo, sweetheart! I didn't know you were out. Where are you?'

'Been to see Ma Handen about that food form. It's called the *E.G.C.*3.'

'Oh, is it! Good for you. How is she?'

'Not too bad considering. I'm afraid I shall be back a bit late. Can you manage?'

'I shall have to, but don't dawdle, buddy; I'm all on my own.' I glanced at my watch. 'Gosh! it's ten minutes to opening time. Snap into it, girl. Bye-bye.' I slung the receiver down, but before I could reach the door the bell rang again. I rushed back. '*Halloa!*'

'Hallo, guv, what are you looking so worried about?

'Eh? Who's that?'

'Pat the cleaner. Why are you looking so worried?'

'How do you know how I'm looking?'

'I'm watching you from over the road. You'll see me if you look out of the window.'

Across the road I saw the door of the telephone box open; and two hands waved up and down through the crack.

'I got Sue in 'ere with me,' came Pat's voice in my ear. 'Like us to come and help in the bars this evening, seeing as you've 'ad a busy day?'

'Eh? Can you? D'you understand the bars?'

'Course we do!'

'Come right over. You're just the girls I'm looking for.'

I ran downstairs to open the side door, and they burst in laughing. First came Sue in satin and sequins, and then Pat in a snappy creation from the British Home Stores. It was the first time I had seen them in their best clothes, and I thought they looked surprisingly smart. When I saw them in the mornings they wore men's dungarees, and had their hair tied in bedraggled head scarves, and Pat was always toothless. Now Pat sported a mouthful of completely lifeless Chinese-white teeth, of which she was immensely proud. Every tooth was perfect. The two rows were as uniform almost as ball-bearings and as unreal as a painstaking and soulless dental mechanic could make them. I could hardly believe my eyes. They fascinated me.

Thrilled, literally to the teeth, by my frank admiration, she parted her lips in an exaggerated smile.

'Didn't you know I 'ad 'em?' she asked naively. 'Nice, ain't they? Better than me own, if you ask me; but I daren't wear 'em when I'm scrubbing the floors else they drop in me bucket.'

'Oh—er—v-very natural,' I stammered trying not to laugh. 'Do you girls know the prices?'

'Course we do, guv!' snorted Pat. 'We always helps Mrs. 'Anden when she's short-handed.'

'Oh!'

'I serve in the saloon, guv,' said Sue, 'and Pat takes the other two bars.'

'Oh, that's fine!' I exclaimed. 'But—er—why are you both calling me "guv"? I'm not the governor.'

'You soon will be,' smirked Pat. '*He* won't come back 'ere. Not *now* he won't, will he, Sue?'

'Not *him*!' grinned Sue. '*He's* after another house.'

'Oh?' said I. 'How d'you know?'

'You'd be surprised what we know,' replied Pat. 'We ain't got cloth ears, have we, Sue?'

'People never thinks of the cleaners down on their knees behind the bars, do they, Pat?' said Sue with a wink. 'It's time we opened, guv.'

'Oh, yes!' I cried. 'Where's Alf?'

'Here I am, mister,' said Alf coming in from another bar and reaching behind the counter for the keys. 'Shall I open up?'

'Yes, please.'

I hurried down into the cellar and turned on the beer while

he unlocked the doors. When I came up again the punctual old woman with the shopping basket was just coming in.

'Oh dear! first again,' she simpered. 'I don't know what you'll think of me. Guinness, dear, please.'

Sue served her and exchanged her empty bottles for full ones without being asked, and then turned to me.

'You sit down and read the paper, guv; you've 'ad a tiring day. Pat and I can manage till the others come.'

'Oh, thanks very much,' I smiled. 'I will.'

Presently Irene returned and joined me; and we exchanged news; and Irene made Sue laugh by telling her about Mrs. Handen's reaction to the gin.

'By the way, did she offer to pay for it?' I asked.

'Well, no,' smiled Irene; 'she hardly had a chance. She fell asleep after the second nip. I suppose we'd better put the money in the till, eh?'

'When did you take the gin?'

'If you mean off the shelf, about five minutes before we closed.'

'Sure it was before?'

'Yes.'

'We should worry, then! It was their own stock.'

'Oh!' exclaimed Irene. 'I forgot that. Aren't stocks complicated! Goodness! I'm tired. Shall we have supper before we're busy? Then we can get to bed early.'

'Yes, let's. I'm dashed hungry.'

'Okay.' Irene went into the kitchen.

'Guv!' shouted Sue. 'Will you come and look at this pump? There's something wrong with it.'

I sighed, and presently located a cracked tube in the cellar. It was a long horizontal one running through two ceiling joists, and very awkwardly placed. Almost an hour passed before I managed to fit a new one satisfactorily. Then climbing wearily up the ladder to the private bar, I found the two Pats quarrelling; and before I realized what was happening they had hailed me as adjudicator.

It was a case of ludicrously petty snobbery, of a barmaid professing to feel slighted at being asked to work with a cleaner. The ethics, if any, of the case were completely beyond my comprehension, but as Pat the cleaner was obviously the injured, not to say the insulted, party, I took her side; but unfortunately without first tactfully soothing the ruffled feelings of the other Pat.

Pat the barmaid flared up.

'Oh, if that's the way I'm to be treated now the governor's in hospital I know what to do. I'm going.' And she went, flouncing to the kitchen for her out-door shoes, and a few minutes later sailed through the lounge again, and with nose in air, passed haughtily into the street.

'Silly little bitch!' I muttered under my breath.

'Pudden?' said Kath the saloon barmaid.

'Nothing,' I replied. 'Only talking to myself. Will you go and take her place in the public bar, dear? I'll stay here with Sue.'

'I'm not used to serving in public bars'

'I'd rather not.'

'Eh!' I choked. 'What's that?'

'I'm not used to serving in public bars,' said Kath primly.

I stared at her, wondering what on earth it mattered to her where she served.

'I'm a saloon barmaid,' she explained.

That didn't help me.

'Well,' I pointed out irritably, 'there are three of us in here now, and there's no one at all in the public bar. Eileen has got the night off. Wouldn't you like to go in there for a change?'

'I'm a saloon barmaid,' she reiterated haughtily.

I was hungry, and tired, and hot under the collar. The summer air was stifling. I muttered a rude word.

'Pudden?' said Kath again.

'Oh, don't keep puddening at me,' I snorted. 'I'm feeling worn out tonight, and it gets on my nerves.'

'I'd rather have my card,' she muttered darkly.

'All right,' I sighed, meaning that she needn't go in the public bar if she didn't want to.

'Pud——! I beg your pardon, Mr. Day!'

'Oh, okay, you can have your card if you want it,' I growled, changing my mind about my meaning.

'Well, reely!' She cocked her nose in the air, and flinging up the counter flap, pranced through the lounge and into the kitchen, slamming the door behind her.

Irene, who was finishing her supper, and had just seen Pat the barmaid flounce in and out, stared at her over the top of the high preparation table.

'Hallo!' she exclaimed. 'What's this procession in aid of?'

'Mr. Day has insulted me, and I want my card.'

'Well, you won't get it at this time of the day,' chuckled Irene.

Kate changed her shoes without another word, and went off with her working ones under her arm. I watched her stalk through the lounge and into the street.

'Well, I'm blowed!' I muttered. 'What's the matter with them?'

'Oh, they get like that,' sneered Sue. 'Barmaids never stop long. You'll get used to it in time, guv.'

Confused noises in the public bar warned me that customers were waiting to be served, so I hurried in there to help Pat; and presently Irene came into the saloon, and finding trade brisk, went quickly behind the counter to help Sue. Later on she asked Sue what was the matter with Kath.

'Oh, the governor just asked her to serve in the public, that's all.'

'But she said he insulted her.'

'Oh, no! It was only that she don't like serving in the public. I can see your husband 'aving the same trouble as Mr. 'Anden had. He could never keep his staff.'

'Oh——? Why not? I thought he was such a considerate man.'

'That was 'is trouble: always too nice to 'em. They don't understand manners. They thought he was soft, and took advantage. Your 'usband don't want to *ask* people to go in the public; not when he's the boss. He wants to tell 'em. "*Go in the public!*" That's the way to talk to 'em. They understand that. The same as a foreman speaks, see? Surly-like.'

'Hmm!' said Irene thoughtfully. 'That's straight from the horse's mouth. I'll remember that.'

'You won't,' smirked Sue. 'You're the wrong kind. You'll always 'ave trouble. Too la-di-da, you two are, by 'alf.'

Irene laughed.

'You can laugh,' chuckled Sue, 'but you know what I mean. You treat 'em as if they was the same as you, and it don't work. Your sort are never any good unless they got good'ns working for 'em.'

'What do you call good ones?' smiled Irene.

'Like Pat and me. Pat the cleaner, I mean, not that other one.'

'I see. Well, I'll think over what you said.'

'You won't,' smirked Sue again.

But Irene did think it over. Fatty Grainger had been kind to his staff, and they played him up all the time; but Mr. Lawson spoke to his as if they were animals, and they worked like slaves and stayed with him for years. Strange, she mused. There seemed to be some sense in Sue's remarks; but even so, could the leopard change its spots?

'I fear me you're right about me and my husband,' she said later in the evening.

But Sue had forgotten the conversation by then.

' 'Ow you going to get on tomorrow without them two?' she asked. 'Pat may be able to stay and help in the morning, but I can't. We can both come in the evening though.'

'Thank you very much,' said Irene. 'I'd like you both to come when you can; and I'll ring the Labour Exchange as well.'

'That's the best thing.'

At closing time, after nothing to eat but three or four minute sandwiches since supper the previous night, I felt past eating, so Irene made me some scrambled eggs, and spread them appetizingly on little squares of buttered toast

—she is quite good at that sort of thing—and I ate them un-hygienically with my fingers while checking the cash.

Before going home Alf asked me for a list of the bottled goods needed for the next day.

'Oh, for the love o' Mike, man,' I cried, glancing up from a wad of notes I was counting, 'can't you look at the shelves and see what's wanted?'

'Yus; but 'ow do I know as you'll agree?'

'Do the same as you did with Mr. Handen. I assure you I won't find fault.

'I'd rather 'ave a list. I like to get things straight.'

' 'Fraid I haven't time to make a list now.'

'Well, it's up to you, mister.'

'It's up to you to do your work, if you want to keep your job.'

'Oh, if it's like that, mister, I'll have my card.'

'Okay.'

'And I'll 'ave it now.'

I continued counting notes.

'Well, what about it?' he asked.

'Go to hell,' I snapped, still counting.

He lit a cigarette and let himself out of the house.

XXIII

THE next morning Irene telephoned the Labour Exchange for two barmaids, and an hour or so afterwards, when I was doing the accounts, the bell rang. I snatched up the receiver.

'White Lark here. Manager speaking.'

'This is the Labour Exchange. I've got a girl here who would like to be a barmaid, but she can only come in the mornings. Is that any good?'

'Yes, send her along.'

'Wait a minute. She's got a baby, and no one to leave it with. Can she bring it with her?'

'Hm . . .? Will it be in a pram?'

'I'll ask her. . . . Yes, it'll be in a pram.'

'Okay, send her along.' I finished the accounts and went downstairs to see if Alf had turned up, and found Irene cleaning the saloon pewter. 'Seen Alf?'

'He hasn't come.'

I told her about the potential barmaid.

'Will that be all right, sweetheart?'

'Better than no one,' she smiled. 'There's plenty of room for a pram in the kitchen.'

'Think Cook will mind?'

'She can go on minding; we must have barmaids. Hallo! there's the phone going. P'r'aps it's the Exchange again.' She ran up to the office and grabbed the receiver.

'White Lark here.'

'THAT MRS. DAY?' screeched a voice.

'*Yes!*' yelled Irene. 'Don't shout; I'm not deaf.'

'I'm only doing me best. It's about Mrs. Rafferty. She can't come. See?'

'Who's Mrs. Rafferty?'

'Why, your Pat, o' course.'

'Oh! The barmaid?'

'No. The waitress what you call Nora 'cos you got two other Pats. Her eldest 'as caught the measles.'

'Oh! That means she can't come for ages.'

'Not while she's isolated.'

'Hell! Well, never mind. Thank——'

'It's all right you saying "never mind", but I done my best and——'

'All right, good-bye.' Irene rang off and dialled the Labour Exchange. 'This is the White Lark. Can you send me a waitress?'

'A waitress? I thought it was a barmaid you wanted.'

'Two barmaids,' Irene replied, 'and now a waitress. The present one's child has measles.'

'Oh, you are in a way, aren't you! Has the girl with the baby arrived?'

'Not yet.'

'She ought to be there by now. How much will the waitress get in tips? They always ask that.'

'Don't ask me; I've only been here a few days.'

'All right, I'll see what I can do.'

Irene returned to the saloon to finish the pewter, and found me putting up the bottled beer. Alf, apparently, had gone for good. Presently the side-door bell rang. I dodged round a barrowload of empties, and opened the door to a small boy.

'Well, my lad, what can I do for you?'

'Please, sir, can I 'ave Mr. Wilton's card?'

'Who is Mr. Wilton?'

'My farver.'

'Oh? And who is your father?'

'Mr. Alf Wilton, o' course.'

'D'you mean Alf the potman?'

'Yus.'

'Well, tell him I can't find his card.'

'Okay, guv.'

As I was shutting the door a man came hurrying along the pavement.

'Good morning, Mr. Day. I'm the firm's accountant. The name's Simpson.'

'Oh, good morning, Mr. Simpson. Come in. What can I do for you?'

'Mr. Bertram will be along presently, and then we'd like you to sign for the house float. In the meantime you and I can run through the books and get ready for him, eh?'

I remembered the incident about checking the safe before opening the house, but decided to forget it.

'Come along, then,' I said, and took him upstairs to the office and showed him the returns for the previous day. 'Yesterday's takings are in that bag,' I told him. 'I'll pay them in as soon as I can spare a moment. You'll find all the books in the desk drawers, and here's the key of the safe. Now, if you'll excuse me, I've got a lot to do downstairs.'

'Er—this is rather unusual,' he muttered. 'You ought to be here while I check the safe.'

'That's all right,' I grinned, 'I know what's in it; it was done yesterday—with a witness—but if I don't get downstairs we won't open on time.'

'Oh? Anything wrong?'

'Half the staff's left, that's all.'

'Ah, that often happens when a new man takes over. They think he's going to alter everything; and they like to show their independence.'

'They're showing it all right,' I grinned. 'Cheerio, I'm just getting the bottled beer up.' I grabbed the bag containing the takings and ran downstairs, to find a very ugly woman of about twenty-six wheeling a pram into the saloon. 'Good morning,' I said. 'Have you come about the barmaid job?'

'Yes, please, sir. I hope Madam won't mind Baby. She's very quiet.'

'Oh, I shouldn't think so,' I smiled, peeping under the hood of the pram. 'Wait here, will you? I'll go and find her. Hm! Pretty little rascal. Takes after her father, eh?' I inquired without thinking what I was saying.

'Yes, everyone says that,' glowed the mother naively.

Irene was dusting the public bar by then.

'I say,' I said, 'that girl with the baby has come. Heaven knows how she managed to get a kid with a mug like hers; but still, perhaps she's got a good heart. You'll find her in the saloon.' I hurried away to wheel the barrowload of empties to the bottled-beer store, and spent the next half-hour wheeling in cases of full

'Takes after her father, eh?'

bottles and taking out empty ones. Then Irene told me she had engaged the ugly woman and prevailed on her to start work that morning.

'Well done,' I said. 'Though goodness knows who's going to teach her the job. By the way, I haven't seen Eileen yet.'

'You won't see Eileen today,' grinned Pat, passing through the saloon with her cleaning gear. 'I seen 'er on a bus for Southend this morning. She'll come in tomorrow with a 'andkerchief round her ankle, and say she sprained it running 'cos she thought she was late, and 'ad to go home again ; or else she'll 'ave another 'eadache or something.'

'Oh, what on earth am I to do !' cried Irene, starting to chalk up the prices for the ugly girl. 'We've only two barmaids this morning—and one of them a learner—and no waitress. Pat, ask Sue to dust Eileen's bar before she goes, will you ?'

'All right, madam.'

Cook came bustling in from the kitchen.

'Mrs. Day, Martha's cut her 'and and gone to 'ave it sewn up.'

'What !'

'Yes, cut it bad, she 'as ; you won't see 'er for another fortnight.'

'Oh, gosh ! And now we've no kitchenmaid.'

'Who's going to do the veges, Mrs. Day ?'

'Don't ask me,' wailed Irene.

'Well, somebody's got to do 'em, ain't they ?' smirked Cook, thoroughly enjoying herself.

Irene fled upstairs and dialled the Labour Exchange.

'Hallo, this is the White Lark again.'

'Oh, yes. Has that girl who wants to be a barmaid arrived ?'

'Yes, I've taken her on. Look here, can you send me a kitchenmaid? I want one at once.'

'Goodness! What's happened?'

'Mine has had an accident and gone to hospital.'

'Oh dearie me! Then you want one right now this minute?'

'Yes.'

'I'll ring you back.'

Irene dashed out of the office, and on the landing met Lizzie the housemaid.

'Oh, Lizzie, Martha has had an accident. Could you go into the kitchen and do the vegetables for her?'

Lizzie stared vacantly, wiping teardrops from the corners of one eye. She was long and thin, and bowed with the weight of years, and gave the impression of being in her second childhood; though actually she never had been very bright.

'Oh, I couldn't, Mrs. Day!'

'What! Why?'

'Not with this cook. She doesn't like me; besides, I'm upstairs staff.'

'But there's been an accident.'

'Oh, I couldn't, Mrs. Day.'

'Not if I ask you as a favour?'

'Not if the Almighty Hisself was to ask me, I wouldn't. I mean, I couldn't; it wouldn't do, Mrs. Day. I'm upstairs staff.'

'Oh, all right,' sighed Irene. She went down to the lounge and peeped into the kitchen, and seeing the cook washing cabbages, backed silently from the door and started to lay the tables for lunch.

'Shall I help with those?' I asked.

'You can put the wooden tops on for me; I'll do the rest.'

'Okay. Have you found anyone to do the vegetables?'

'Ssh! Cook's doing them. Don't take any notice or she may stop.'

Mr. Bertram bustled in.

'Good morning, Mr. Day.'

'Heck!' I muttered to myself. 'Good morning, sir.'

'Mr. Simpson here?'

'He's upstairs, sir.'

'Right, let's go up.' Mr. Bertram led the way to the office. 'Good morning, Mr. Simpson. Everything in order?'

'Yes, sir,' replied Mr. Simpson. 'The cash is four shillings up.' He pointed at two florins on the blotter.

'Good!' said Mr. Bertram, pocketing the two florins.

'Would you like to run through the books, sir?' Mr. Simpson asked, with a surreptitious wink at me.

'No,' replied Mr. Bertram, whose knowledge of book-keeping was roughly on a par with Irene's knowledge of cooking. 'Not if you and Mr. Day are both satisfied.'

'I'm satisfied,' I said.

'Right,' smiled Mr. Bertram. 'Lock the money away and sign for it.'

I hurtled the cash into the safe and turned the key.

'Where do I sign? Here?' I scrawled my signature, and glanced at my watch. 'We open in three minutes, sir.'

'Right you are.'

I dashed downstairs, grabbed the keys from the board, and rushed round the house opening doors. Irene went into the saloon to initiate the new barmaid into her duties. Mr. Bertram sauntered downstairs, and came to the counter as I hung up the keys.

'I'd like to see the cellar, Mr. Day.'

You would!—I thought—my gosh, you would!

'Okay, sir, you know where it is,' I smiled, turning to take an order. 'Three bitters and a mild-and-bitter? Right you are.'

Flinching slightly at the cavalier treatment, Mr. Bertram went thoughtfully down into the cellar. Five minutes later he came up again, and mumbling a brief, 'Well, you seem busy: I'll go,' went off in a huff, taking Mr. Simpson with him.

'What's up with Bertie?' Irene asked.

'Dunno,' I said. 'I'm too busy looking after his blasted money to dance attendance on him. He ought to know that.'

Cook came rustling up to the counter.

'Mrs. Day, someone'll have to help with the veges else I'll never get 'em done in time. I got the puddings to——'

'All right, all right,' groaned Irene, 'I'll see what I can do.' She ran up to the office and dialled the Labour Exchange.

'This is the White Lark again. What about that scullery-maid?'

'D'you mean kitchenmaid?'

'Yes; I don't care what you call her.'

A laugh came over the wire.

'Well, I've got one here; but I don't know whether you'll have her.'

'Why? What's the matter with her?'

'She's like the barmaid I've just sent you: she's got a baby too.'

'Well?'

'Well, do you mind?'

'Do I *mind*!' A short mirthless laugh escaped from Irene. 'Listen,' she said, 'I don't care if she's got triplets; and I don't care if she's not married. Can she peel potatoes and prepare cabbage?'

'Yes, and she can come now if she may bring her baby.

'Right! Speed her on her way.' Irene ran downstairs to lay the rest of the luncheon tables.

Presently a dark-haired pasty-faced woman of about thirty, with a sad expression and faithful-looking canine eyes arrived complete with another pram and baby. Irene left the table she was laying and hurried her into the kitchen.

'What's your name, dear?'

'Eileen.'

'Right, we'll call you Maisie; we've got another Eileen— at least, we did have yesterday.' Irene helped her to park her pram next to the other one, and then led her to the sink and put a peeler in her hand. 'There you are, Maisie, snap into the spuds. We'll talk business afterwards.'

Maisie picked up a potato and started to peel it as if she had been there all the week.

Irene filled a tray with cruets and took it into the lounge. She heard the telephone ringing upstairs, and glanced at the clock. It was getting late. She looked into the saloon. I was nowhere in sight. Probably down in the cellar, she thought. She ran upstairs.

'LIZZIE!' she shouted.

'Yes! Here I am.'

'Answer the phone, will you?'

'Oh, I couldn't, Mrs. Day.'

'Eh! What's that! Don't be silly; it doesn't bite. Just pick it up and say "hallo". Someone's bound to answer you.' Irene ran down to the lounge again and distributed the cruets. Then going into the kitchen for cutlery, she came across the eight-weekly. 'Oh gosh! I'd forgotten all about this. I say, Cook, there's a job for you here. The eight-weekly. It's two and a half weeks overdue.'

' 'Snot my job.'

'I thought you always did it for Mrs. Handen?'

'Maybe I did, but I don't see 'ow I'm going to find time now. You know I'm leaving on Saturday, don't you?'

'What!'

'Madam's 'ad me notice.'

'This is the first I've heard of it.'

'Well, I 'ad no call to mention it to you, did I? I only give me notice in on Friday.'

'Mrs. Handen didn't say anything to me.'

'Probably thought I wouldn't go.'

'Well, it doesn't give me much time to find a new cook does it? I hope Mrs. Handen gives you a nice reference when she finds you've left without filling in the eight weekly.'

'Oh, she'll give me a good one all right. I'm going along to see her on Sunday. Lemme see now, what 'ospital did you say they was in?'

'I didn't say,' smirked Irene going into the lounge to finish laying the tables.

Later on she went into the saloon to help at the bar and think things over. Cook was leaving on Saturday; and this was Wednesday; and the eight-weekly was more than a fortnight overdue—and it was supposed to be in the post. She mixed herself a gin-and-French to help the thought process. Perhaps Bill could fill it in. She took it for granted that she couldn't do it herself. Sneaking into the kitchen under the pretext of getting some more cutlery, she smuggled it out to the lounge, and glanced through it. It was entirely incomprehensible to her. She brought it into the saloon and showed it to me. I put on my glasses and perused it woodenly for several seconds, and then with much ruffling of my hair

or several minutes; but it meant nothing to me at all. My
glasses fell off of their own accord, thus confirming Irene's
worst fears.

'Sorry,' I said. 'It might be written in Chinese as far as I'm
concerned. I can't even understand the explanations.'

'Oh, darling! Can't you try?'

'Can't try any harder. You know what I am: I'm con-
genitally incapable of filling in forms. I'm allergic to the
things. I can't even do football permutations. Besides, we
don't know how far Cook has been cheating.'

'How d'you mean?'

'Well, common sense tells you you couldn't run a lunch
trade if you filled this up properly. I'm not such a fool that
can't understand that much. You'd never get the food.'

'Oh . . .! Well, what do we do?'

'You'll have to get round that blasted cook somehow.'

'Oh, wouldn't it be lovely to be a barmaid and have no
worries! I wonder if they realize how lucky they are.'

Someone rapped on the counter.

'Sorry,' said Irene and I together.

Presently Irene noticed Lizzie hovering in the background.

'Yes, Lizzie, what is it?'

'The phone. It was a gentleman for Mr. Day.'

'Oh, yes? What did he say?'

'He said he 'ad to go away and could he speak to Mr. Day,
and I said Mr. Day was too busy owing to being short-
handed.'

'Oh!—did he leave a message?'

'Yes, he said Mr. Day couldn't come till Thursday; and I
said Mr. Day was already here serving in the saloon bar;
and he said his name was Mr. Harry Day. And I said "Oh,
I suppose you must be his brother." '

'Oh . . . ? Crikey ! Yes ? What then ?'

'He asked me if we had a mooring on the line.'

'A what ?'

'A mooring. "Is there a mooring on the line ?" he says. Twice he asked that ; and I said I didn't know, and should I go down and ask his brother.'

'Gosh ! What did he say to that ?'

'He wouldn't answer, so I put the thing down and come down to ask you.'

'All right, Lizzie. Thank you very much.' Irene turned to me. 'Hear that ? I wonder if it was important. Any Harry Days in your family ?'

'Not that I know of. Hallo ! there's the phone again. I'll go.' I ran upstairs and snatched up the receiver. 'White Lark here.'

'That you, Mr. Day ?' came Mr. Marnes's voice over the line.

'Yes, sir.'

'Thank heaven for that ! Who's that confounded moron I've just been talking to ?'

'That was Lizzie, the housemaid.'

'Good lord ! You'd better keep her away from the phone. Look here, I want you to do something for me. There's a man coming from the brewery tomorrow to inspect your place. His name is Garroway, and——' (I chuckled.) 'What are you laughing at ?'

'Lizzie said his name was Harry Day.'

'Oh ! Well, this fellow is rather a big shot, and we always arrange for a director to show him round when he visits a house, but the three of us are due at a meeting tomorrow D'you think we can leave him to you ?'

'Oh, yes, sir ?'

'I could ask Mr. Bertram to come, but—er—well, Mr. Kent and I thought that you, Mr. Day, in your inimitable way—er—don't you think so?'

He was a tactful old blighter.

'Leave him to me, sir,' I said, grinning to myself at my end of the wire.

'Good! Excellent! Mention that I've written to apologize for not being there.'

'Yes, sir.'

'But don't tell him anything else. Just take him down into the cellar, and let him see the kitchen if he wants to; and there's no need to discuss takings or—or anything. Understand?'

'I understand, sir. I'll send him away happy.'

'He may want to stop to lunch, so——'

'He shall have the juiciest bit o' beef, sir.'

'That's the way, Mr. Day. You've got the idea. Well, I'll leave him to you. Don't let him pump you. Good-bye.'

I went downstairs, to find Irene busy with a brainwave. Shd had just caught herself gazing at a fat woman who was enjoying a glass of Guinness with considerable gusto. Guinness! The life-blood of cooks! Here was the solution of the food-form problem. Snatching a bottle, she made straight for the kitchen.

'Here you are, Cooky. I think you need this after your strenuous efforts with the vegetables. How's Maisie doing? All right?'

Cook coloured up.

'Oh! Oh, thank you, Mrs. Da—er—madam. Thank you, madam. I'm sure I always do my best.'

Irene beamed. She had been promoted from Missis to Madam.

'I'm sure you do, **Cook,**' she lied; 'and I'm very grateful. It makes life so pleasant when everyone pulls together, doesn't it?'

Cook flushed again; and Irene, passing into the lounge and taking a last look at the luncheon tables, thought to herself, 'That's fixed the old cow; she can't very well refuse to fill in the *E.G.C.*3 now.'

Through the doorway beyond the saloon counter Pat's form could be seen flitting between the private and the public bars. Irene paused a moment and listened to her perky voice as it came floating through to the lounge.

'It won't 'urt you to wait, mate. If you was to drink less your old woman might 'ave a pair o' shoes without 'oles in 'em. All right, Ma, 'ave the right money ready. Wazzat, you? Well, I only got one pair o' 'ands, ain't I? Here you are, love, fourpence change. Wish they was all as polite as what you are. . . .'

I was pretty busy too. The new barmaid had just given three consecutive customers short change and jammed the till. Irene hurried to help me.

'You fix the till, cocky; I'll deal with these men.'

'Thanks.' I went to the till and gave it a mighty smack in the Mr. Lawson manner, and to my surprise everything clicked into place. Feeling very efficient, I turned and beamed at the customers.

Meanwhile Irene had switched on her charm.

'Now then, you three big men, don't frighten the poor little girl. You can see she is only a learner; and she's trying her best.'

The three big men glowered unchivalrously, being unable to believe that such an ugly 'poor little girl' could even have a best to try. In their opinion only the prettiest of barmaids were allowed to give short change, and even then ... However, Irene soon adjusted matters.

Then a familiar fanfare sounded, and in came Enid, wearing a linen creation by Dior in tulip-leaf green and flake-white, with a hat to match, and waving a jade cigarette-holder in cheerful greeting.

'Hallo, you two! I say! this is a nice pub, isn't it? Quite cosy.' She came to the counter and murmured in an undertone, 'Customers are a bit scruffy though, aren't they, for this neighbourhood?'

'Well, we're a bit off the beaten track,' I explained. 'It's quite slummy down the hill.'

'Yes, I suppose it is. Where are the er-rums? What are they like? Any good?'

'Both in hospital,' replied Irene.

'Oh?'

We explained about the Handens' accident.

'Well, well, well!' smiled Enid. 'You don't say! So you're managers now, are you?'

We nodded.

'What an amazing chunk of good fortune! Rather bad luck on the er-rums, of course. And you say they're nice people?'

'Absolute darlings,' said Irene.

'Oh! I'm sorry for them, then. What a shame! Pity it couldn't have been the Lawsons, isn't it? Er—I think some people at the end there want serving.'

Irene and I were kept busy for a few minutes. Then we told her about our staff situation.

'Anything I can do?' she asked.

'You could bank yesterday's takings for me,' I replied.

'Righto.' She did that, and returned with an idea. 'What about me for a waitress, Bill? I'll serve the lunches for you.'

'What! in that rig-out?' I laughed. 'You'd have all the men trying to date you up, and the women scowl——'

'Well, that's good for trade, isn't it?' she interrupted. 'I'll go and see your cook. Where's the kitchen? Through there?'

'The door on the left,' I grinned.

Enid tripped through the lounge.

'Oh, stop her, Bill!' cried Irene.

'No fear!' I said. 'We want a waitress, don't we? And she can get round Cook to do the eight-weekly for you.'

Enid disappeared into the kitchen; and Cook, glancing up from a mixing bowl, saw her standing by the hot-plate staring at the babies in the prams.

No one had told Enid about the babies.

'Goodness!' she exclaimed. 'I didn't know you had a crèche here. These belong to the customers, I suppose . . . ? What a brilliant idea!' She caught Cook's eye. 'Hallo, Cook! I'm the new waitress.' She noted Cook's blank expression. 'Oh, are they your babies! Sorry.'

'Eh! W-what! I been a widow for nearly ten years.' Cook glared at Enid. 'You from the Labour?' she inquired incredulously.

Enid had never heard a Labour Exchange called the 'Labour'; and in some involved way she connected the word with babies.

'Eh!' she cried, startled. 'Labour? Me! No; I'm a widow too. Er—Mr. Day wants me to be the waitress today. I'm his sister.'

'Oh! I thought you wasn't from the Labour. Well—erm—there are the pads, on that little table there.'

Enid examined one of them.

'Mm—yes—I've settled enough of these in my time.' She glanced down at her frock. 'Got an apron you can lend me?

This is a Dior and I don't want to spot it. Phew! Isn't it hot in here! Like a cool drink, Cook?'

Cook began to think this was one of her days. Her face blossomed into smiles.

'Well, I wouldn't say no to a Guinness, madam.'

'Guinness?' blinked Enid. 'Bit heavy in this heat. Wouldn't you rather have——'

'Oh, I never drink anything but Guinness, madam.'

'Righto. What about the girl by the sink?'

'Maisie! Madam wants to know what you'd like to drink.'

'Oo! I never drink, thank you.'

'Have an iced lemonade,' Enid suggested.

'Oo! it makes me hiccup,' giggled Maisie.

'Well, a nice lemon squash, then,' said Enid temptingly. 'That's cooling and not gassy.'

'Oh, well, I'll have a small port.'

'Good heavens!' gasped Enid. 'Well, please yourself; I'm having a nice cold John Collins.'

Mr. Green had arrived while Enid was in the kitchen, and when she returned to the saloon to get the drinks she saw him talking to me. He had seen her come in from the lounge; and after watching her go to the counter, he stepped back for a better view.

She leant across the counter and whispered to Irene:

'Who is the piggy-eyed man with Bill, who's giving me the once-over?'

'Oh, that's Mr. Green from our head office,' muttered Irene under her breath; 'but we don't really know what his job is.'

'Hm! Nasty bit o' work.'

'Shall I put these drinks on a tray for you?'

'Yes, please.'

Mr. Green watched Enid disappear into the lounge on her way to the kitchen, and then winked at me.

'That's a nice bit o' homework, Mr. Day. Does she come here often ?'

I suppose it was silly of me, really, to take offence at hearing my sister called a 'nice bit o' homework'; because after all it was meant as a compliment, even if the expression was a trifle vulgar.

'Can't say I've noticed her,' I muttered, flinching slightly, and purposely glancing at a very ordinary-looking woman who was just coming in from the street.

'Not that one !' snapped Mr. Green. 'The one who has just taken a tray of drinks into the lounge.'

Then the humour of the situation struck me.

'Oh, her !' I grinned. 'That's the new waitress.'

He glanced up suspiciously, as if suspecting me of pulling his leg; but I, being tired of his company, said nothing to ease the situation; and after I had refused a glass of bitter, knowing full well a double whisky would be expected in return for it, he became tired of my company too, and left.

All the same, Enid was a great success as a waitress; almost a riot, in fact, though bitterly disappointed at the amount of her tips, until Irene pointed out that most of the customers probably guessed she was connected with the management.

'Oh, was that it !' she murmured doubtfully. 'Well, any-way, what do I do with the tips? You haven't a tronc here, I suppose ?'

'No, no tronc,' I grinned; 'you keep them. They're yours; you earnt 'em.'

'Oh, I couldn't ! I'd feel funny. You take them. They may

e useful one day when your cash is short.' Eventually she
arked the money in a mug beside the saloon till.

After we had closed the house she had her own lunch with
rene and myself in the deserted lounge. We two, being used
o public-house fare by then, ate ours with a relish born of
ong hours and hard work; but poor Enid, who numbered
mong her friends the *maîtres d'hôtel* of some of the most
xclusive caravanserais of Europe, found the curled shavings
f warmed-up beef somewhat weary going.

'How does Cook *get* it like this?' she asked querulously.

Irene explained the frugal system of roasting meat the day
efore and then hardening it in the refrigerator so that it
ould be carved into the thinnest of slices.

'It's to make the joints go a long way,' she added a trifle
uperfluously.

'I see,' said Enid. 'Well, I must say she's got this thin;
nd it certainly goes a heck of a way. But surely, Irene,
ou'll alter all that now, won't you? I mean, this tastes like
ough cork.'

'Oh, yes!' cried Irene enthusiastically. 'You bet we will!
Ve're planning a tip-top West-End cuisine at popular prices.
'll pay like anything; and then we'll get our salaries raised,
ee? Of course, we'll have to get a good cook.'

'Naturally,' murmured Enid masticating pointedly.

'I mean, one who can manage as well as cook,' explained
rene, slightly on the defensive. 'That's half the battle.'

'Mm—all the battle,' muttered I unkindly.

Enid glanced tactfully at the clock.

'I'll have to go when we've finished lunch. I've several
ings to do this afternoon. Like me to come and wait
omorrow?'

'Yes, please,' glowed Irene and I together.

XXIV

ALF had combined the duties of potman with the cleaning
of the cellar, but as he now seemed to be permanently absent
without leave, the latter unpleasant task devolved on me.
So the next morning, on noticing that a long stillion running the whole length of one wall was occupied only by
empty casks, I decided to pull it out and clean the floor
underneath, and donning a pair of bedraggled flannel
trousers and a cellarman's ankle-length leather apron, set
to with hose and stiff broom. This, be it understood, was
before breakfast and while I was still unshaved. Imagine me,
therefore, dressed as described, with sleeves rolled above
dirty elbows, dark smudges on bristly cheeks, and breathing
imprecations into the beer-laden air, a slave to duty, forgetful of time, and deaf to all but the rasp of a stiff broom on
the wet cement and my own disgusting language. Then,
seeing a shadow pass across the floor at about half past ten
o'clock, I looked round, to observe a little man dressed in a
black jacket and striped trousers standing with his back to
me at the foot of the ladder.

'Hallo !' I exclaimed. 'Where did you spring from ?'

'Good morning,' said he doing an about-turn. 'Good
lord ! Major Day of all people ! What the——'

'Cripes !' I cried. 'If it isn't that old beggar Garroway.
Well, I'm damned ! How are you, old boy ?'

We gripped one another's hands, and pump-handled
them up and down the way two old comrades-in-arms do
when they meet for the first time as civilians.

'What on earth are you doing down here?' he gasped as soon as we had grown tired of shaking hands.

'Cleaning the ruddy cellar, of course, you old stiff!' I replied. 'Can't you see?'

'I thought you were a rubber planter.'

'So I was, but I'm a perishing publican now. I'm the manager here.'

'Good lord! I never realized it would be you.'

'And I never connected you with your name either. Well, I'm beggared! And so you're a comic cellar inspector, are you?'

'Well—er—hup! Er—hardly that.'

Then I saw I had offended the silly little blighter; and at the same time remembered that, anyhow, I wasn't frightfully fond of Captain Garroway. But you know what it is when two old soldiers meet: they fall on each other's necks even if they have hated one another's guts for practically an entire war. Not that I actually hated Garroway. It was just that I had never been able to get on with him; I couldn't understand his outlook on life. He was a lean ascetic-looking little man of about forty, with thin lips and a domelike forehead; rather the successful parson type. If he had plumped for divinity instead of beer he'd have been odds on for a pair of gaiters before he was fifty merely on his looks. Not a bit my sort, or, for that matter, the kind anyone would ever have dreamt of connecting with a brewery; but the trouble now was that I had been told to suck up to him; and, of course, during the war he had had to call me 'sir', and here was I looking like the twin brother of Alf the potman—and to a pompous ass like him that was a reversal of positions impossible to resist. Also, although I didn't know it then, he had it in his power to be very useful to me. Any

H

other kind of man would have thought the situation too intriguing for words, and antied up to the hilt; and my directors would have thought how wonderful I was to have got on with him so well. Which would have done me a power of good. But I had offended him.

There was only one thing to do: get back to the old comrades-in-arms status as quickly as possible. I glanced at my watch. It was later than I thought. Twenty-five minutes to opening time. That again was typical of Garroway: he had ignored the age-old maxim of the licensed trade which lays down that it is bad manners to visit a publican when his house is closed.

'I say, old boy,' I said, 'it'll soon be opening time. I must nip up and get clean. When you've had your squint round the cellar fiz up to the saloon and tell the wife to give you a drink. I'll warn her you're coming. Shan't be long, old man.'

'All right, Day,' he replied coldly.

I scrambled up the ladder, thinking as I climbed that in the public-house trade one always seemed to be missing meals, and also that I didn't quite like the way Garroway had called me 'Day'. Too patronizing, I thought, and savouring a trifle much of the manner in which I had called him by his name on certain occasions when he was my junior officer. Not so good.

In my bath I pondered that matter deeply; that is to say, as deeply as a man can ponder when he has missed his breakfast and has only a very little time to spare. But I never have been able to complete my toilet in less than three-quarters of an hour, even when in a tearing hurry. However, I was able to cogitate long enough to remember that when dealing with twerp types a slight glow of alcohol tends to divert one from their major defects; so when, some twenty minutes or so after opening time, I felt fit to face the world, I made my way by a roundabout route to the spirit store, and after injecting myself with a generous shot of anti-twerp dope, made my way to the saloon, trying to look as if I had touched nothing stronger than tea that morning.

On entering the saloon, I saw at once that Irene didn't like Garroway. It was obvious by the set of her shoulders as she leant across the counter. She looked so pleased with him that only a drivelling idiot would have believed it. However, she seemed to be putting herself over in the right way; and the anti-twerp dope was doing me a bit of good; and a moment later the three of us were clustered round a trio of glasses containing sherry for Irene and bitter for Garroway and self. Nothing would induce him to take anything stronger than beer.

'How long have you been managing here?' he asked presently, peering into my whisky-sparkling eyes.

'Only a couple of days.'

Between us, Irene and I explained the full situation.

'I see,' he said. 'Ever thought of buying a place?'

'Not enough cash, old boy.'

'Well, why don't you apply for a tenancy?'

'Even that requires a fairly hefty amount, doesn't it?' I asked. 'I mean, the way everything is rising in value nowadays.'

He shook his head.

'Not if the brewery likes you. We have our own method of valuing.'

'Meaning . . .?'

'That you ought to come and see me at the brewery.'

'Why? You got some 'fluence, old boy?'

'That's my job.'

'Eh! What is? Dishing out tenancies?'

'Yes.'

'Cripes! Why the heck didn't you say so before! I'd have bought you a bottle of champagne.'

He smiled.

'Get your people to send a relief couple along one day, and both of you come and see me. Don't worry too much about money. Breweries are very decent with people they know.'

'But the brewery doesn't know me.'

'No—but I do.'

'Oh—oh, lovely!' I began to wonder if I had been mistaken in Captain Garroway.

Then a bunch of customers came in and Irene and I had to go and serve them. When we came back to continue the conversation another bunch came in.

'Excuse me, old boy,' I muttered, grabbing a couple of mugs. 'By the way, you're stopping to lunch, aren't you?'

'Sorry, I don't think I can.'

'Oh! Well, you want to see the kitchen, don't you?'

'No. Shan't bother. As far as I can remember, "A" Company's cook-house always used to look pretty snappy. Eh? Remember that time when the Old Man . . .'

We were off. I forgot all about the customers; but try as I would, I couldn't get him to have another drink. That was him all over. I remembered he used to go right through a sergeants' mess dance on half a pint of mild ale. And did they love him for it! I don't think! Anyway, he buzzed along presently; but the next day when I telephoned Head Office to get a day off for Irene and me to go and see him at the brewery I was turned down flat. Nothing doing till after the holiday season because there were not enough relief couples. That was to be expected, of course, and in my opinion nothing to worry about because we had a lot to earn before we were ready to venture our tiny capital; but Irene was very annoyed. She said she believed in striking while the iron was hot. I agreed, but pointed out that as we couldn't do anything about it we might as well forget it for the time being and hope for the best.

'Anyway,' I added, 'I'm definitely under the impression that you don't like the squirt.'

'I don't,' she admitted; 'but that's no reason why we shouldn't use him; and I have a feeling that if things hang fire he'll remember he doesn't like you.'

'Mm—quite!' I agreed.

'And what's more,' she continued, 'I'm convinced it was only because he was carried away by meeting someone he'd served with in the Army that he offered to do anything for you at all.'

'Er—quite!' I agreed again, wondering where she picked up her uncanny knowledge of masculine human nature.

However, to get back to the White Lark, on Saturday the cook left; but not, I am glad to say, before filling in the eight-weekly—under dire threat of an appalling reference from Irene, she and I having wisely kept the name of the Handens' hospital a dead secret. All the same, we were left with little time to think of Garroway and a tenancy.

Then, to add to our troubles, Irene found when she telephoned the Labour Exchange that cooks were in short supply; so she had to do the cooking herself. I did offer to do it for her, but she was up in arms at once.

'No fear!' she cried. 'I'm pulling my weight in this job. Don't you worry about me.'

But she worried, herself. Particularly about the sweets, or

what our customers called the 'afters', because she and I had
always favoured savouries. In other words, Irene had never
made a pudding in her life. However, she had a stroke of
luck. Nosing in a store cupboard for something or other
she discovered a gross of tinned marmalade puddings that
Mr. Handen had picked up cheap somewhere, and Mrs.
Handen had forgotten.

Her first luncheon session passed off surprisingly well,
except that two regular customers who had ordered Irish
stew complained their soup tasted of Irish stew; but that
was merely because that was almost exactly what it was. She
had utilized the remains of a previous Irish stew to make the
soup—which, incidentally, after adding a few handfuls of
pearl barley, she called Scotch broth. Which struck me as
being rather clever.

'Oh, sorry,' she muttered, gulping slightly. 'It's the new
cook. She didn't know what we were having today; but it
will be all right tomorrow.' Though how she would make it
all right tomorrow she did not know, because (a) she was
the new cook, and (b) she had been rather hoping to concoct
all her soups in much the same easy manner.

She put the problem—in a very tactful and roundabout
way, of course—to Maisie, the new kitchenmaid (of the
faithful canine eyes), who promptly suggested a nice vegetable soup.

'Everybody likes that, madam, and it's easy to make.'

'Can *you* make it?' cooed Irene encouragingly.

'Oh, yes, madam. I make a lovely vegetable soup.'

'Good for you!' cried Irene. 'Snap into it tomorrow, girl.
You put the stuff in the pot, and I'll stir it for you.'

By the end of Irene's first week as cook all the regular
customers were complaining of a surfeit of marmalade

pudding, and she was at her wits' end to know what to do
about it. Even my flair for cooking was no use in this case;
but again Maisie came to the rescue, remarking ingenuously
that she liked making puddings.

'Maisie, you're a godsend!' cried Irene. 'You're a veritable
deus ex machina.'

'Yes, madam,' smiled Maisie, blinking intelligently.

Maisie was soon doing nearly all the cooking (after a
fashion, but nevertheless better than Irene could do it) and
also staying behind each afternoon to prepare the vegetables
for the next day. By that time a new waitress and two barmaids had come and gone, and a new potman had been
engaged and discovered leaving the house with his pockets
bulging with miniature bottles of spirits; and he also had
left.

Meanwhile, Irene spent her every spare moment tele-
phoning the Labour Exchange, and I spent my every spare
moment searching the columns of the *Licensed Victuallers'
Gazette*, and writing advertisements, and sounding customers for likely friends; and, needless to say, both of us
grew daily more sympathetic towards Fatty Grainger and
his staff troubles at the Block and Anchor.

A fortnight after the Handens' accident Irene and I were
offered, and accepted, the management of the White Lark,
and I signed an agreement to that effect, with the usual
clauses regarding three months' notice on either side, or
summary dismissal for ourselves for drunkenness, theft, and
so forth. We didn't think a heck of a lot of the place, but on
the other hand, the way it was offered made it hard to
refuse, and anyway, we thought it wise to accept; also, of
course, we needed the extra money.

Then, in due course, came our first stocktaking, and a

week or so after that, a visit from Mr. Bertram to inspect the house. In place of his usual cheery greeting—'Well, and how's the White Lark today? Everything all right?'—he surprised me with a terse 'Good morning, Mr. Day. I'll inspect the cellar.'

Wondering what was the matter, I followed him down the ladder, and after breaking a foreboding silence with several tentative coughs without result, ventured a curt 'Anything wrong, sir?'

'Yes; we've just had the figures for your first stocktaking.'

'Oh! Not up to standard, sir?'

'Very much below standard, Mr. Day.'

'Oh. Er—how much below, sir?'

'That's a question we never answer.'

'Oh!—well then, how the—I mean, what the——'

'They'll have to be much better next time, Mr. Day, or . . .'

'Oh—er—mm.'

'You remember the wording of your agreement?'

'Oh, absolutely,' I murmured; though, being a hundred per cent allergic to 'whereases' and 'aforesaids' and interminable sentences devoid of commas, I had hardly glanced at the thing. Nevertheless, I guessed what he meant. 'But all the same, sir,' I growled, 'it doesn't help a lot if one doesn't know how much the stocks were short.'

'We don't aim to help you: we pay you to manage.'

'Oh. Oh yes, quite; but all the same——'

'I'll go up and see the books.'

'Oh, all right, sir.'

After examining the books, and twirling his handlebar moustache thoughtfully at some corrections, he glanced at the safe.

'Cash all right?'

'Oh, yes, rather!' I was happy about the cash; there was a surplus. 'I had ten and fourpence over this morning,' I burbled brightly.

'*What!*'

'I mean at the first check, sir. The ten bob was a slip, of course. Only fourpence up now.' It seemed that, in view of the aforementioned corrections, the surplus was best forgotten. I hoped I would be forgiven for the white lie.

'Hm!' he muttered. 'Well, we're giving you another chance as it's your first stocktaking, but the next time—you understand?'

'Yes, sir.' And how I hated calling him 'sir', although actually I liked the little blighter in some ways. However, we'll drop that subject.

'Good morning,' he said.

'Good morning, sir,' said I.

He stalked out of the office, leaving me standing in the middle of the room a prey to conflicting emotions. The inspection seemed to have ended. Presently I drifted sadly down to the saloon. It was a bit heartbreaking, especially as I'd thought I was going to make such a dashed fine publican.

'Hallo,' said Irene. 'What's up with Bertie?'

'Why?'

'Only that he's just blown out of here looking so frightfully pleased with himself.'

'Eh? What! Pleased with himself . . . !'

'Yes. Has he been knocking you about?'

'Knocking me about? That little runt! What d'you mean?'

Irene laughed.

'Well, he looked as if he'd just won a fight; and when I

was listening-in to the two of you in the cellar, all I could hear were growls from him followed by "ohs" from you.'

'Oh, he was telling me the stocks were short.'

'What! *Ours?*'

'Of course, you ass! Whose d'you think?'

'But, how much?'

'He wouldn't tell me.'

'Then, how the hell are we to know how serious it is? Or where to start tracing things?'

'That's what I wanted to know, fathead!'

'The silly fool! I expect it's a gag. That's why he looked so pleased when he went out.'

'I wish I thought so.'

'Hm! The silly nit!'

We consoled ourselves with a double gin each, and continued the consoling process with several more double gins, and eventually had a miserable lunch and spent the afternoon quarrelling: I maintaining that the stocks really were short, but Irene insisting that it was merely a gag to keep us up to the mark.

After the next stocktaking (the following month) Mr. Marnes called to inspect the house, and in reply to my inquiry told me the stocks had righted themselves, adding casually, in response to my uplifted eyebrows, that they did that sometimes; which, of course, called forth loud guffaws from Irene when I reported the matter.

'I told you so,' she smirked.

But I remained unconvinced. In my opinion we were the wrong types to be treated like that, and I credited the directors—wrongly perhaps—with the intelligence to realize that we weren't cheating them ourselves, and also, that we watched our staff just as sedulously whether the stocks were up or down; though perhaps 'sedulously' was not quite the right word, because we did trust them to a certain extent. However:

'Don't be a fool,' snapped Irene. 'They judge us by themselves.'

In the meantime the staff situation remained the same, and how we would have managed without Pat and Sue it is hard to conjecture. Barmaids and potmen came and went with monotonous regularity; and it was the same with waitresses. A new cook went off at the end of her second day because Irene thoughtlessly asked Maisie's opinion on some minor point instead of hers. And so it went on.

At the end of September, when the holiday season was over and I wrote to Garroway for an appointment, he wrote back to say he was just off to France for three weeks. In reply to my next letter he said he was booked to the hilt for another month—'Getting rid of the holiday accumulations, old man.' (Loud guffaws from Irene.)

Then we forgot all about him in the pressure of work; because the public-house business wasn't turning out a bit like we expected. We thought we had picked a soft job with lots of people to wait on us; and here we were doing all the work ourselves, and not a soul to do any waiting. Even Lizzie the housemaid had popped off with pleurisy, the poor old thing! And although Pat and Sue did their best to fill in the gap there was still no one to bring our breakfasts upstairs. We didn't mind having our lunch—which, by the way, had now developed into our main meal of the day—in the lounge with the customers; but to have to eat our breakfast there, in the stale beer-laden air of morning, with Pat and Sue scrubbing the oilcloth round our ankles and interrupting our conversation with cockney wisecracks, was a bit much, quite apart from the smell of their dungarees.

The only thing that consoled us was the knowledge that our sales were steadily increasing. At the end of six months we had enlarged the turnover by approximately twenty per cent. We put this down entirely to clear bitter, full measures, and—to use Mr. Handen's expression—not messing about too much with the mild ale. We were even more particular than he was, especially with the ale—and the full measures! Also, we didn't cadge for drinks. That made quite a difference. The Handens, it may be remembered, liked to make a bit on the spirits. And the word went round the district. We knew that by the comments of the customers. For example, they remarked frequently, and glowingly, on an order of mine which ensured that spirits were measured on the counter, and not at the spirit stand with the barmaid's back turned to the purchaser. But unfortunately no credit accrued to us from the directors, because our commission was solely on food sales, and was so small that it was not worth considering. In fact, we ignored it, the same as the Handens had done, although, curiously enough, our luncheon trade did increase, not however because of the high standard of the cooking—even Irene admitted that— but merely because there were more liquor customers to stay and eat. In passing I may mention that as far as we knew then, or even know now, managers of public houses never draw commission on sales of alcoholic drinks; though I cannot state this for a fact. Anyway, it has probably been assumed by now that we were getting fed up with the job, but that was not strictly the case. We liked it well enough—up to a point, as Mr. Handen would have said—but we were missing the gentlemanly appreciation of good work done, to which we, or rather I, had been accustomed in the East. Admittedly, we were not getting the percentage per barrel mentioned by Mr. Handen, but we had considerably increased the aggregate profits of the house; yet, every other month the directors saw fit to flog their willing horses—meaning Irene and myself—by saying the stocks were short.

The lunatic part of all this, as I see it on looking back, was that I was inclined to believe them. It was no use Irene nattering to me about the directors not being sahibs, and pointing out that they thought it just ordinary good business to flog their willing horses so as to get even still more out of them. I couldn't believe grown men could be so foolish. When I had found a coolie on the plantation doing work above the average I had put his wages up above the average, to encourage the others and so on; and when as a result of this, and in spite of the larger wages, the plantation owners had found their margin of profit widening they had done the same with my pay—to the happy benefit of all concerned, including the shareholders.

I refused to believe that one had to be a gentleman to understand such simple logic, though I do now; and one day when Irene found me filling myself with gin because Marnes had been along to tell me our stocks were short again, she blew up. She'd had her basinful. And honestly I couldn't blame her; and in the end, had to admit she was right and I was wrong.

'Pah!' she snorted. 'I do wish you'd shut up about the stocks. I keep telling you it's just a gag to keep us up to the mark. It's a pity we can't get a tenancy of our own.'

'Yes,' I agreed, 'but look how prices have rocketed. With

our skimpy bit o' capital we could hardly find a place the size of a hencoop.'

'Oh, skip it,' she said. 'Can't we find a house that's been badly treated, and get it cheap and build up the trade?'

'Hmm! we might,' I admitted gloomily. 'Anyway, I'm fed up with this perishing firm, and their short stocks and righted stocks, and short stocks and righted stocks; and especially with Bertram, blast him! He's been to a decent school and ought to know better. And I'm fed up with that blasted fellow Green always borrowing money, and guzzling double whiskies which he expects me to "make up", as he calls it. Why should I cheat for him! And I'm fed up with the firm's spies, and having too many bosses. In fact, I'm fed to the teeth with the whole shooting match.'

'So am I,' chimed in Irene, 'especially with the staff, and having to slave sixteen hours a day doing their work for no pay. I hate the working class. I thought we were going to have an easy time, with lots of servants.'

'Same here,' I muttered. 'That was the chief attraction of the job. I thought a publican's hardest work was trying to laugh at naughty stories he'd heard ten times before; but, dash it! I haven't heard one for weeks. Haven't had time to listen. But it's the stocks that get me down.'

'Oh, why worry about them! It's just a gag. Our trouble is, we started too well.'

'But they said our first stocktaking was bad.'

'I know, darling, but that was just routine. They tell everyone that.'

'Oh, I don't know! The Lawsons said their stocks were never bad; and he was knocking back at least a bottle of whisky a day at the firm's expense. And Fatty Grainger kept his wife and all their relations in drinks at the firm's expense; and he never said anything about his stocks being short. And we're paying for nearly all our drinks.'

'I know, darling, but we're not watering the beer.'

'That's true; but nor did old Handen.'

'No, my pet, but think of the money his Maggie made on her gin racket. And d'you think Mr. Green never spotted that! Eh?'

'Hmm! Well, what if he did? What are you getting at? D'you think the firm expects us to cheat?'

Irene sighed.

'Darling, you're so simple. Can't you realize you're not a sahib in the East now? You're in England. I think the firm takes it for granted that every manager cheats; and they expect to get their rake-off. Fatty told you, you couldn't be honest in this line, didn't he? And he watered his beer by the gallon to cover his shortages and leave a bit over for himself, and perhaps a bit more for the firm too. The Handens sold bottles and bottles of gin twice over, and probably watered the stuff as well at week-ends when there was no fear of an excise officer walking in, and probably the mild ale when you weren't looking! And the Lawsons had two sets of prices, and fiddled short measure on the spirits and kept a percentage of the snack takings for themselves. It's no use saying we've increased the turnover. The directors can see that with half an eye; they've only to look at the books; but they don't work that way. They go by percentage per barrel, like Handen told you. They know they can get so much for a bottle of spirits if you give so much short in the gin-and-limes; and so much for a barrel of beer if you sell the dregs—otherwise what's the utilizer for!—and a bit more if you add some water on Saturday nights; and they want just that much for themselves in each case. If any cheating is being done, they're going to be in on it—whether the turnover is increased or not.'

'Do you really believe that?'

'My good man, if you don't believe it you ought to be psycho-analysed.'

'Oh!' I smiled. 'Well, perhaps I'd better be done anyway, because we've been spending more than our measly wages ever since we started on the job; so we're not saving anything towards our own pub. And I'm not going to cheat for anyone. Not even for ourselves.'

'Okay, get busy hunting for a tenancy, even if it is only as big as a hencoop; and if you like I'll sell the house, and perhaps we can get one as big as two hencoops. Then there will be no point in cheating; because you know why the trade has increased here since we took over, don't you?'

'Of course. Clear beer and full measure; and especially full measure.'

'Exactly; and clear mild ale! Don't forget that. And that's the way we'll have it when we get our tenancy. To hell with fiddling a few pence on each barrel, even if we make a little less per barrel. You remember, that's what Handen said himself. He said you have to decide whether to increase your trade or save on the farthings, because you can't do both.'

'Yes, I remember; and he was right. I suppose the trouble is, the directors are such crooks themselves that they just can't bear to see anyone fiddle a farthing. They'd rather lose money. Ah well! we live and learn.'

'Yes,' chuckled Irene. 'I'm glad you are learning at last. Now you can start writing letters again. What will you do? Begin at page one in the directory and carry on till you strike lucky, like you did last time?'

'I suppose so.'

'Well, don't forget you write to breweries now, not licensed caterers.'

'Leave it to me, girl. And I think I'll wake Garroway up again.'

'Hmm!'

'What do you mean by that?'

'Bit of a blob, isn't he? Besides, he's remembered he doesn't like you. But still, you did soldier together. What about ringing him up and saying "Look here, you *sinna-sathi pandiandi*, when the heck are you going to fix your old major up with his *tallu kadde*?"'

'Yes, that's what I meant. It's about time he did something, especially when I remember the number of times I failed to tick him off when he deserved it; and after all, his job is giving away pubs. I'll do it now, and accost him on those lines.'

I went up to the office and grabbed the receiver.

'That you, Garroway? . . . Day here. Look here, you low-down stiff, I'm getting fed up with you; you're name'll stink at the next reunion when they hear what I've got to say about you. What d'you think you're doing, keeping me waiting all this . . . What! . . . Oh, all right, but if we can't make that date you'll have to . . . Okay, okay, old boy, I'll be ringing you.'

XXV

IN due course we went to beard Garroway in his den. The brewery was approached through huge wrought-iron gates set in an archway big enough to take three or four London buses in line abreast. Beyond the gates were acres and acres of cobble-stones piled high with towering heaps of barrels. And not a soul in sight.

'Goodness!' exclaimed Irene. 'Why are all these barrels left out here?'

'Don't ask me,' I replied. 'Perhaps the wood has to mature or something.'

'But won't they rot if it rains?'

'Dunno; I'm not a cooper. Seen a brewery anywhere?'

'Not a glimpse. We might be in the middle of Sahara.'

We wended our way between two forty-foot high heaps of barrels, and came upon an enormous Hercules-type of man smoking the thinnest cigarette I'd ever seen in my life.

'Good morning,' I said.

'Good morning,' said he.

'Know where Mr. Garroway's office is?' I inquired.

'Eh? 'Oo?'

'Mr. Garroway.'

'Never 'eard on 'im.'

'Oh!'

I glanced at Irene. She and I were under the impression that Garroway was a person of importance in the brewery.

''Oo is he?' inquired Hercules affably. 'Nothink to do with deliveries, is he?'

'No. Tenancies.'

'Oh, I wouldn't know nothink about that. Follow me, mister, I'll show you where you can find out.'

We followed him round another mountain of barrels and came to a large factory-like structure of red brick surrounded by a village of office buildings.

'Go in there and ask at *Inquiries*. They'll tell you where to go, mister.'

'Thank you.'

We went in.

'Good morning,' said I to a man with a pencil behind his ear. 'We have an appointment with Mr. Garroway.'

'Mr. who?'

'Garroway.'

'Who's he?'

'We've come to see him about a tenancy.'

'Oh, this is cooperage. Try the *Inquiries* next door.'

I went in there, leaving Irene outside.

'Good morning. I've an appointment with Mr. Garroway.'

'Eh?' exclaimed a man dressed in a white linen jacket and striped trousers. 'Who?'

'Garroway.'

'Oh, Harringay the surveyor. You the chap from the Sewerage and Water Catchment Board?'

'No, I'm not. I want to lease a house.'

'Oh, I beg your pardon; I don't know anything about that. We're all chemists in here. Ask at *General Inquiries* by the main gate.'

We plodded back to the main gate and found a little shack that we had missed on our way in, and stumbled irritably over the mat into a tiny waiting-room.

'We have an appointment with Mr. Garroway.'

'Oh, you from the Sewerage and Water Catch——'

'No,' I snapped. 'We've come about a tenancy.'

'Sorry, I thought you said "Harringay". You're after a shop, eh?'

'Shop, no! A public house, man. This is a brewery, isn't it? We want to lease a——'

'All right, don't get het up; we call public houses shops.'

'Oh. Well, where do we find Mr. Garroway?'

'Er—have you an appointment?'

'I've just told you we have.'

'Oh, yes, of course. Well, you know where to go, don't you?'

'No, that's what we've come to ask you.'

'Oh—er—yes, I see. Well, it's rather hard to describe. Just a minute.' He put his head through a doorway. 'Smith!'

'Sir?'

'Take this lady and gentleman to Mr. Garroway's office.'

A spindly-legged youth suffering with acne appeared, and we followed him out to the cobble-stones again.

'This way,' he muttered. 'Arter a shop?'

'Yes,' I replied.

'What 'ouse you got now?'

'We haven't one.'

'Blimey!'

'What d'you mean by that, lad?'

'You'll 'ave to stand up to 'im, that's all. He's a rum'n, this Garroway.'

'Oh! Is he!'

I felt my morale deteriorating rapidly. This maty hob nobbing of the office boy gave me the impression that publicans seeking tenancies were very minor luminaries in the licensed trade. He spurted ahead, and after hurrying

hrough several cobble-stoned lanes between dirty red-brick
uildings to a house at the back of the factory—which
urned out to be the brewery—showed us into a gloomy
nte-room with a row of chairs against the far wall and a
arge mahogany table in the middle.

'What's the name?' he inquired off-handedly.

'Mr. and Mrs. Day.'

'Right. I'll tell 'im you're 'ere.'

He went down a passage and disappeared into a room,
while Irene and I sat on chairs against the wall. Presently
e returned.

'He says you're late.'

'Well, we've been hunting for his office for twenty
minutes.'

'All right, he'll let you know when he wants you.
Don't forget what I told you. Stand up to 'im. Good
 uck.'

'Thanks. Good-bye.'

By this time I had no morale left at all; and Irene was
uming.

'Doesn't anybody ever call anyone "sir" in this place?'
he asked angrily.

'Not if the anyone happens to be a prospective tenant,
pparently,' I muttered.

'The cheeky little brat!' she growled.

'Oh, I dunno,' I said. 'I think he liked us.'

'Huh!' she snorted. 'Think we might have a cigarette?'

I glanced at the mahogany table.

'There are no ashtrays about. P'r'aps we'd better wait.'

'Oh, all right.'

A door opened, and a man and a woman came slinking
ong the passage, and left the building muttering out of

the corners of their mouths. Irene and I exchanged wonde
ing glances. Then the door opened again, and Garrowa
appeared.

'Oh, there you are. Come in.' He waved us to two chair
and sat at his desk. 'Well, here you are,' he said casually.

'Yes, here we are!' said I brightly.

Then there was a short pause, and Irene piped up.

'Yes, here we are,' she smiled.

I gave her a cigarette, and offered my case to Garrowa

'Er—well, I suppose it's all right with you,' he mutter
self-consciously. 'I mean—er——'

'What's up, old boy?'

'Well—er—I suppose it's different with you.'

'What are you gassing about?' I asked. 'Have a cigarette

'Well—erm—in the office, you know . . .!'

Then it occurred to me that he was telling me smoki
was prohibited. My hackles rose. The idea was too fantasti
I was still wondering why he hadn't offered the cigarett
himself.

'Listen, cock,' I said, 'are you trying to tell me we ca
smoke in your office?'

'Well, it is unusual, Day, for tenants to smoke in t
brewery.'

I flared up. I mean, that struck me as being so damn
silly, especially between two old comrades-in-arms. Fan
not being allowed to smoke in a brewery office, of
places!

'All right,' I snorted, pausing to strike a match and lig
Irene's cigarette, 'take that ashtray off your desk.' Ther
passed him my case again.

He flushed and took a cigarette.

It was a bad start, but I felt there were limits to t

ngths a man could go for the sake of his future. However,
beamed matily to suggest I thought he was only joking.

'Now,' he said, 'tell me, what capital have you?'

'Not a lot,' I grinned, and told him. There is no point in
ating the amount now, because values change so quickly
owadays.

'Hmm!' he said. 'You won't get a very big shop for that;
nly what you might call an average-sized one; that is, if
ere is such a thing as an average-sized public house.'

Then the three of us spent a pleasant ten minutes or so
ith Garroway naming public houses of roughly the size
btainable with my limited capital, and Irene and I saying we
idn't know them; then five or six more minutes with Irene
nd I recalling pubs of a size we thought he meant, and he
ying he didn't know them; until eventually one of us
ought of a pub we all knew and which was the right size.

'Hm!' I said. 'I'm surprised my skimpy bit o' capital is
ough for a place as big as that. I mean, considering how
operty has risen in value during the last few years.'

'Oh, we have our own way of valuing our houses,' he
plied.

'Oh?'

'We have to.'

'That's useful.'

He made no reply to that, so I drew my own conclusions.

'The next thing is a broker,' he said.

That was a new one on me.

'Eh?' I said.

'We can't deal direct with you, you know,' he smiled.
'ou must have a broker.'

'What for?'

'We only deal with tenants through a broker.'

'Why? What's the idea?'

'It's the custom,' he replied, smirking at me as if h
thought I was a fool to ask the question.

'Oh!' I frowned. I didn't like the sound of that. It re
minded me of Mrs. Lawson and her quaint old Englis
customs; but still, I didn't see that I could do much abou
it. 'How does one get a broker?' I asked.

He went all self-conscious with himself.

'Well, as a matter o' fact I've already spoken to a ma
about you. Of course, you needn't have anyone I suggest
you—er——'

'That's all right, old boy,' I interrupted. 'I can trust you
After all, we were soldiers together.'

'Well, would you like me to ring him and ask if he can se
you now?'

'Carry on, old lad.'

He reached for the telephone receiver, and a lot of 'ol
boying' went on for several minutes about matters of n
concern to us. Then suddenly he said:

'Oh, by the way, I've got that couple here. You know, th
chap I told you about and his wife. Could you see them no
if they come over? . . . Righto, I'll send them along. By
bye.' He turned to us. 'He can see you now. I've got one
his cards somewhere. Here you are. Well, cheerio, Da
Best of luck. Good-bye, Mrs. Day.' He stood up.

Apparently that was the end of the interview. Irene and
thought it had only just started. We had learnt nothing at a
about the relationship between brewer and tenant, exce
that the latter was not supposed to smoke in the former
office; which still rankled with both of us; or what kind
leases we had to sign or anything. However, the intervie
was over, so we stood up and smiled politely, and went ou

The broker was called Kurrens, and his offices were only a few hundred yards away from the brewery. He was a round smooth-faced man who looked as if he shaved several times a day. He pointed to two leather-covered chairs, and sat down at his desk, and after much struggling managed to cross one fat leg over the other, and then stared at us with a pair of steel-blue eyes. There was no friendliness in the stare. I took an instant dislike to him.

'Er—Major Day?' he murmured.

'Mister,' said I. 'I don't use my rank.'

'Oh-ah.' He glanced at Irene. 'Mrs. Day?'

Irene smiled.

He nodded, as if pleased to learn we were married; whereupon Irene took a dislike to him.

'Mm-ah,' he mumbled, and looked at me. 'Lemme see, you want a shop, is that it?'

'Yes, please.'

'Friend o' Garroway's, eh?'

'That's right.' I began to loathe him.

'In the Army together, weren't you?' he asked, as if he didn't think a heck of a lot of the Army.

I nodded, and he let that sink in.

'Hm—well, what sort o' house d'you want? How big? You got some capital?'

'Oh, yes, I have——'

'Did Garroway tell me how much you got?'

'Shouldn't think so. He didn't know till half an hour ago.'

'Oh. Mm—how much did you say it was?'

I told him the amount.

'I see,' he said patronizingly. 'And where are you now?'

'The White Lark at Gladstone Park.'

'Managing?'

'Yes.'

'That's one of Kent and Co.'s, isn't it?'

'That's right.'

'Hmm! Have you told them you're looking for a shop?'

'Not yet. Bit early, isn't it?'

'Mm—maybe, if you're a friend o' Garroway's,' he mumbled, thoughtfully dusting his waistcoat. 'How long you been with Kent and Co.?'

'Oh, quite a few months.'

'And you haven't told them you're looking for a shop. Mm!—I see.'

'Why? Do you think I ought to?'

'No-no. Plenty o' time. Right you are then. Keep in touch, won't you?'

'Eh?'

'Drop me a line now and again, or come and see me if you like.'

'What about?'

'Well, you want me to find you a shop, don't you?'

'Yes, that's what we're here for.'

'Well?'

'Well, what?'

'That's all. Nice to have met you. Good-bye.' He stood up, and strolling to the door flung it open.

Irene, taken by surprise, passed out of the room in silence, followed by myself, also in silence; and both of us in a sort of daze. Half-way down the stairs we came to.

'So that's what they call a broker!' I exclaimed.

Irene muttered a rude word.

'D'you think he'll find us anything?' she asked.

'Do you?' I countered.

'Not a thing.'

'Nor do I,' I growled. 'What did Garroway want to put us on to a louse like that for? I'll ring him up when I get back.'

'Oh, save your breath,' spluttered Irene. 'What's the time?'

'Five past twelve.'

'Let's go and see Jack Summers at the Three Kings.'

'Yes—that's an idea! We need advice about this.'

The Three Kings was our local at Greenheath, and Jack was quite a pal of ours. He was an ex-officer, like myself, and the chap, it will be remembered, who told us you could get housemaids in pubs if you called them cleaners. We arrived at about one o'clock; and when we told him about the interview with Kurrens we thought he'd never stop laughing.

'You know who he is, don't you?' he asked.

We shook our heads.

'He's Kent and Co.'s broker.'

'Crikey!' I exclaimed. 'What did Garroway want to put us on to him for?'

'Don't ask me, old boy. Garroway is your friend, not mine. I don't like the little squirt.'

'Oh! D'you know him?'

'Sure. I went to him for a shop once, but he wouldn't give me one.'

'Would you believe it!' said Irene. 'And did you start as a manager like we did, when you first came into the business?'

'Yes, the same as you two, with a firm of licensed caterers.'

'Were your stocks ever short?' she inquired.

'Every other month,' grinned Jack, 'the same as yours are, I suppose.'

'And what did your wife say?'

'The same as you, I expect.'

Irene shot me a naughty glance.

'Tell me, old boy,' I said, getting back to the business in hand, 'what are brokers for?'

'Ah!' Jack told us. 'Well, you see, old man, you've got to face it, but brewers don't think a hell of a lot of publicans as businessmen. They seem to think we're inclined to drink too much occasionally, and get scatterbrained, and forget things; and the broker's job is to see that we keep our various licences up to date, and so on, so that we don't get into trouble with the magistrates and the temperance crowd and —and all that. Get me? And he keeps an eye on our accounts, and audits them, and deals with the income-tax people, and shows us where we are making or losing money, and advises us on all legal matters connected with the trade; and if we do get into trouble he engages lawyers who specialize in the trade to fight for us. He's a sort of paid uncle, and father confessor to us on all business matters; but his real job, of course, is to protect the brewers. That's why they insist on us having one.'

'And who pays him?' I grinned.

'Oh, we pay him, of course, you ass! Have a bit o' sense. The brewers aren't that dumb. Though I must say a good one is almost worth it. I mean, he's a chartered accountant, and well up in the law; and he daren't let you down or he'd get in bad with the brewers, which would be the end of him. All the same, if you get one who doesn't like you, or a dud'n, it's the devil. But there aren't many duds; the brewers see to that. They have to.'

'I see. And what's the Kurrens fellow like? D'you know him?'

'No—only heard of him, but he's no good to you; he's your firm's man, and they're big enough to dictate to their broker. I mean, think of the money he's drawing from them, with—what have they got? Fifty houses, isn't it? Lord! What a job! The softest on earth. It wouldn't pay him to fix one of their managers with a shop; not without asking them first. They might fire him and save his commission—and the brewers would be on their side. I mean, they're big noises. It's not a strain on the intellect to understand that, is it?'

'No; but why did Garroway put us on to him?'

'Don't ask me, old boy. Perhaps you weren't kind to him when you were his senior officer in the Army. You should have thought of that, you silly nit. However, if you want a good broker who likes your type I can put you on to one; not my own man, of course, because I want him all to myself, as far as can be, in spite of his fondness for double whiskies. And can he knock 'em back! Oh, boy! And not a farthing off me income tax to cover 'em. If I could drink like him and do figures at the same time I'd be a bookie and make a fortune. By the way, you know I've got another house besides this one, don't you?'

'No; that's news to me, old lad.'

'Oh! Well, I have, and I'm negotiating for a third, and he's getting it for me; so you see I don't want to put anyone else on to him. You realize you have to queue for pubs nowadays, don't you?'

'Seems pretty obvious; yet some people say there's a slump coming.'

'Hope there is. It'll give chaps like you and me a chance to get in cheap. You've noticed, haven't you, there's a best pub in every town or district? Well, you nip in somewhere

and get hold of one of 'em, or the second best, and make
something of it. You won't lose money, old boy, slump or
no slump. This is our chance.'

'Oh! . . . then you believe there is a slump coming?'

'Positive! I'm building on it. Ask me bank manager. How
ever, about this broker I've just mentioned. He's looking
for a chap like us: you know, ex-officer and all that, for a
particular house he has in mind. How about it? Shall I ring
him up?'

'Yes, please do.'

XXVI

THERE is no point in writing a long-winded account of the negotiations for our first house. Suffice to say they ended well over three years ago, and the broker Jack Summers recommended was most helpful. What we would have done without him we can't think ; he is now our firm friend ; and today we have three flourishing houses. There is a slump in the trade, but as each of our houses is the best in its district we are far from worrying.

Irene sold our home at Greenheath, and we now live in an old-fashioned inn-cum-hotel on the outskirts of a small country town within easy car ride of London, where I am writing this in our head office. Pat and Sue, the resident barmaids, can be heard arranging glasses in the saloon for the evening session, while Pat's husband, the bar-cellarman, turns on the beer. Sue's husband, our chauffeur-gardener, is pottering contentedly among the marrows and cucumbers in the greenhouse ; and in the scullery the ever faithful Maisie (of the canine eyes) can be heard singing light-heartedly as she washes her child's clothes. No one knows where her husband is, or cares much ; least of all Maisie who, as kitchen-laundrymaid, is now able to support herself and her child in comfort without the worry of providing beer and betting money for a bone-idle consort.

Upstairs in the office, to where all these pleasant sounds are percolating, Irene stands by the open window smiling happily at me over the top of the auditor's—or, if you prefer it, the broker's—report on the last year's trading of

W. & I. Day & Co. (Licensed Caterers) Ltd. She looks ve
pleased. Equally pleased seem Rubbertumi and Kinkibo
who with stomachs distended by fieldmice, are sleepi
peacefully under a cherry tree in the garden, complete
unperturbed by any thought of the ghastly amount
income tax we two shall have to pay.